The English Glee

Edited by

PERCY M. YOUNG

Music Department
OXFORD UNIVERSITY PRESS
Oxford and New York

Oxford University Press, Walton Street, Oxford OX2 6DP, England

Oxford University Press, 200 Madison Avenue, New York, NY 10016, USA

Oxford is a trade mark of Oxford University Press

The front cover includes a reproduction of A Madrigal *by John Callcott Horsley (1817–1903), son of William Horsley and godson of John Wall Callcott (both of them composers featured in this collection). Reproduced by permission of the Bridgeman Art Library/Bury Art Gallery and Museum.*

Printed in Great Britain by
St Edmundsbury Press Ltd, Bury St Edmunds, Suffolk

Contents

INTRODUCTION v

no.	title	composer/author	voices	page
1	The Love Rapture	Arne/Anon.	ATTB	1
2	Death's Final Conquest	Battishill/Shirley	SATB	8
3	The Rose	Bayley/Watts	SATB	18
4	The poor soul sat sighing	Beckwith/Shakespeare	SATB	22
5	Thyrsis, when he left me	Callcott/Gray	SATB	28
6	Hark, the Lark	Cooke/Shakespeare	SATB	38
7	Susanna and the two Elders	Cooke/Prior	SATB	45
8	Long may live my lovely Hetty	Cooke/Johnson	SSTB/SATB	54
9	Lady Anne Bothwell's Lament	Corfe/Scottish folk-song	SATB	61
10	Ring out ye crystal spheres	Crotch/Milton	SATB	65
11	The Nightingale	Danby/Anon.	SATTB	71
12	Take, O take those lips away	Elliott/Shakespeare	SATB	78
13	Slow, slow, fresh fount	Horsley/Jonson	ATTB/ATBB	85
14	O Poesy	Horsley/Rowe	SSATBB	93
15	Here in cool grot	Wellesley/Shenstone	SATB	99
16	Hail! Hallow'd fane!	Wellesley/Anon.	SATB	106
17	Elegy for Cymbeline	Nares/Shakespeare	ATB	114
18	Poor Barbara	Shield/Shakespeare	SATB	120
19	Merrily push round the glass	Shore/Irving	TTB/TBB	124
20	Ring out ye crystal spheres	Smith/Milton	SSATB	127
21	Under the greenwood tree	Smith/Shakespeare	SATB	138
22	Hail! smiling morn	Spofforth/Anon.	ATTB/ATBB	153
23	Doubt thou the stars are fire	Stevens/Shakespeare	SATB	160
24	Ye spotted snakes	Stevens/Shakespeare	SATB	163
25	When from the skies divine Cecilia came	Valentine/Moore	ATB	172
26	Divine Cecilia	Webbe Sen./Congreve	STB/SAB	178

Introduction

In *English Glees and Part-Songs* (1886) William Barrett claimed that 'the glee is one of the two forms of composition [the other being the anthem] to which English musicians can lay claim without fear of rivalry or dispute'. The glee was the vehicle by which secular part-singing was carried in the period between the deaths of Handel and Mendelssohn. Its descent was from the madrigal—by way of the informal society organized by Nicholas Yonge in the late sixteenth century—and its successors, and the lively contents—especially catches and canons—of the popular collections of Thomas Ravenscroft, John Hilton, and John and Henry Playford. Such music was in the first instance cultivated by lay clerks and choral vicars as respite from the rigours of professional duty. According to John Earle they were a 'bad society and yet a company of good fellows, that roar deep in the quire, deeper in the tavern. Their skill in melody', he continued, 'makes them the better companions abroad, and their anthems abler to sing catches.'[1] The common singing-man played a great part in the creation and cultivation of a new tradition of social harmony.

The glee came into being alongside the catch, and like the catch was both cause and consequence of sociability. The normal venue for its practice was the inn, and the agency for its promotion, according to English convention of the eighteenth century, was a club, whose membership was male. On this account the music practised, in the first place, was in the form of 'three-man songs', for alto (counter-tenor), tenor, and bass. Catches and canons rejoiced in a rude virility. But in the period in which the glee became dominant texts were preferred which reflected not so much the literary tastes of the tap-room, but those of the upper level of middle-class readership. In response, composers on the one hand freed the glee from the limitations imposed by three vocal parts and often scabrous texts, and, on the other, extended its scope to suit textual requirements by disposing contrasts of rhythm, dynamics and texture in interrelated sections or miniature movements.

By the middle of the eighteenth century societies of various kinds were ready for a new and congenial type of secular music. How such bodies proliferated in the North of England is shown by the subscribers to Thomas Hale's aptly titled *Social Harmony* (1763), a collection of male-voice part-songs intended primarily for masonic lodges by (or arranged from) Purcell, Handel, John Travers, Thomas Arne, William Hayes, and many others. Hayes, whose contribution was an *Ode Sacred to Masonry*, was at the time Professor of Music at Oxford, where he was much occupied in promoting amateur as well as professional music-making. In 1766 he published a volume of *Catches, Glees, and Canons*, in the Preface to which he explained how such music could happily combine pedagogic purpose and moral philosophy:

> Many [of his pieces] were born under the happy Auspices of a most agreeable and well regulated Society that met weekly . . . [in Oxford], and which I found to be productive of the most desirable Effects: viz, Cheerfulness and Good-humour, Friendship and a Love of Harmony; not to mention how much it contributed to the Improvement of the younger Practitioners, enabling them to sing readily at Sight, by being accustomed to a variety of Cliffs and Movements, and this, not by Compulsion or Drudgery, but, by Allurements, and the Gratification of a Pleasure they found in it themselves.

Hayes went on to hope that such 'little detached Pieces of Vocal Harmony' would be welcomed by his 'Brethren of Cathedrals', and helpful in contributing to 'the just execution of Church-Music'. Whether all his 'Brethren of Cathedrals' were quite so idealistic is to be doubted, but glees were certainly pleasurably, and profitably, sung and composed by lay clerks, vicars choral and organists.

In due course the character of the classical glee came to be determined democratically, by secret ballot. In November 1761 the Noblemen's and Gentlemen's Catch Club had been formed in London for 'the encouragement of the composition and performance of canons, catches, and glees'. It was also a dining club, meeting on Tuesdays between February and June, at the Thatched House Tavern in St James's Street. At these meetings works that had been submitted for consideration for the prizes that the club offered were sung and the winning entries determined. The several categories were catch, canon, 'serious glee, cheerful glee, and [for a few years only] foreign glee'. The secretary was Edward Thomas Warren, who held office from 1761 to 1794; during that time he kept copies of works submitted and also published the winning entries. From the beginning a number of prominent professional musicians were invited into 'privileged' membership of the club, among them Arne, Hayes, John Beard, Jonathan Battishill, Benjamin Cooke, Samuel Arnold, and Samuel Webbe the elder—Warren's successor as secretary.

In 1766 the Anacreontic Society was founded, whose membership consisted of 'Peers, Commoners, Aldermen, Gentlemen, Proctors, Actors, and Polite Tradesmen'.[2] The regular members, as in the

[1] John Earle, *Microcosmographie* (1628), XLVII, 132–3.

[2] *GM* (May 1780), 224.

Catch Club, admitted professional musicians as honorary members. There being a greater stress on the pleasures of the table, and less on the quality of the music, and still less on the propriety of the words that were sung, the main claim to fame of the Anacreontics lies in the membership of John Stafford Smith, whose *Anacreontic Song* terminated every meeting, and of which the melody, long after the decline of the society, took root in the foreign soil of the United States.

Of the many societies in the country that supported the performance of catches and glees, one in particular merits notice on account of its place in social history. This was the Musical and Amicable Society in Birmingham, established in 1766, which functioned to some extent as an insurance society, so that out of the members' weekly contributions what remained after the cost of music and other expenses had been met supported payments in case of illness, or to the nearest of kin of any who died (with their subscriptions up to date).[3]

For various reasons—musical, commercial, and moral—the restriction of glee-singing entirely to male gatherings seemed neither possible nor sensible. A new direction was indicated by the publication of Samuel Webbe's *The Ladies' Catch Book* (*c*.1764), 'the words of which will not offend the nicest delicacy'. This was the first of many such collections. A few years later progress on the domestic front is recorded in the young Fanny Burney's account of an amusing evening in 1777 spent in Gloucester, singing glees with her cousins:

> After supper, Richard, James, Betsy, and Mrs Wall sang through some catches [she means glees], indifferently enough upon the whole, though I like the voice of Richard very much on these occasions. Mr Berkeley sometimes joined the treble part, and Dr Wall [of Worcester] the bass, but so ludicrously as to make me laugh immoderately. Richard gave himself a thousand droll airs, in the Italian way, squaring his elbows, making faces, heightening his eyebrows, and acting profusely.[4]

In the club conditions that generally obtained, the problem of a 'treble' part in glees with more than three parts was otherwise solved by one singing falsetto, by the occasional engagement of a professional soprano, or by the conscription of choir boys. Sometimes the results were less than satisfactory, as John Marsh relates of an occasion in Canterbury in 1783:

> Besides Mrs Goodban [the star singer of the city and wife of an inn-keeper, whose premises were used by glee-singers], one had a choice of ten men and as many boys, belonging to the [cathedral] choir. As to the boys, they were so badly taught by Porter, their master [and cathedral organist], that out of so many it was difficult to find even two fit to sing a simple song, and even the upper part of a glee to support her: on which account when we came to try over the glee of Dr Harington for a treble, tenor, and bass—'Gentle airs' at the rehearsal, Mr Porter brought three boys, to sing the upper part, saying, that, if they were not enough, I might have more; to which I replied, that, as it was for a glee, not a chorus that I wanted them, one, or at most two would be sufficient.[5]

During the last quarter of the eighteenth century the cult of the glee in London was extended through societies that were based on the principles of the Noblemen's and Gentlemen's Catch and Glee Club (as indeed all glee clubs of any pretension long continued to be), but under the control of musicians. On 22 December 1787 a glee club, growing out of a group of 'Professors and Amateurs of eminence' which had been meeting informally at a house in St Paul's Church Yard since 1783, held its first meeting at the Newcastle Coffee House. The president was Samuel Arnold.

The next development, of a more professional 'Graduate Meeting', is described by John Wall Callcott:

> At an accidental visit paid to J. Beard Esq[re] at Hampton in August 1790 by Dr Arnold, & Dupuis, Messrs Callcott and [Robert] Hudson the conversation on the journey happened to turn to the late establishment of the Glee Club & the rapid success which an institution of barely three years date had found [with] the number of candidates exceeding that of the 30 members. Dr Dupuis, a principal in the formation of the Glee Club and who had given the Society the name it now bears, suggested the idea that the musical Graduates were sufficiently numerous to constitute a select party & which might be held alternately at the house of each member at equal distances of time throughout the year.[6]

Apart from the initial refusal of Benjamin Cooke to join this organization on account of his displeasure at being displaced as conductor of the Academy of Ancient Music by Arnold, the Society of Musical Professors progressed amicably through 1791. Cooke swallowed his pride (and his dinner!) at the house of Dr Parsons on 22 June. In the meantime the industrious Callcott had made the acquaintance of, and had had some lessons with, Haydn, who was then in London. Haydn—who, on account of his Oxford doctorate, conferred on 8 July, was *de facto* a member of the Society—was unable to attend either of the next two meetings, but on '28 October the presence of the new member was highly gratifying to all' (BL Add. MS 27693, fo. 17). At the first opportunity during the next season, Haydn (who had also been a guest of the Anacreontics) entertained the Graduates to dinner 'on the 20th June at Parsloes [Coffee House] in St James's St. to which at his particular request Mr Salomon was admitted partly as an intimate friend of Dr Haydn, partly as an interpreter, Dr Haydn having not made sufficient progress in the English tongue.'[7] During this visit to England Haydn added accompaniments to the Earl of Abingdon's *12 Sentimental Catches and Glees.* Echoes of the English glee are evident in the

[3] *Birmingham Mercury* (7 December 1895).

[4] A. R. Ellis (ed.), *The Early Diary of Fanny Burney, 1768–1778* (1913), 2 vols, II, 185.

[5] John Marsh, *Journal*, CUL Add. MS 7757, vol. 9, 839.

[6] BL Add. MS 27693, fo. 6.

[7] Ibid., fo. 16.

Lyrische Blumenlese, which he composed soon after his return to Vienna.

The involvement of Haydn with English music drew attention to the end of one era and the beginning of another. One school of glee composition, moving alongside tendencies in poetic behaviour which considerably influenced musical character, began to make way for another. Many composers, while not entirely forgetting the long tradition of bawdy song, developed a keen appreciation of trends in literature and drama. In an age of Shakespeare editions and production methodology there were few who failed to set lyrics from the plays. These settings, with Arne at one end and R. J. S. Stevens at the other—and Benjamin Cooke, John Stafford Smith, James Nares, William Paxton, William Shield, and composers of the amateur Oxford group intervening—variously reflect eighteenth-century attitudes to Shakespeare. William Collins, James Thomson, and Thomas Gray compelled the attention of some composers, while John Stafford Smith and William Crotch set Milton in splendid resonance. William Shenstone, who on one occasion described a set of his poems as 'madrigals' and was the 'greenest' of the poets of that age, was an inspiration to others.

Jonathan Battishill, Benjamin Cooke, John Stafford Smith, and John Wall Callcott, all avid book collectors, were outstanding in their appreciation of literature. Callcott, coming to the peak of his skill and influence at the point at which the aesthetics and emotions let loose by Wordsworth and Coleridge came to a climax, expressed himself in a manner consistent with the Romantic temper at the turn of the century. Indeed, Callcott was well acquainted with Coleridge, from whom, in 1807, he borrowed manuscript copies of Italian songs. In the following year while Coleridge's contribution to the lecture series of the Royal Institution was a paper on 'Poetry', that on 'Music' was delivered by Callcott. Like his friend and mentor Benjamin Cooke, Callcott was assiduous in his cultivation of the antique. He foresaw the coming significance of folksong and ballad, and he was a powerful exponent of the dark moods of Ossian. On 23 September 1798—long before Schubert and Loewe—he made the first setting (for three voices) of *The Erl King*, a bad (anonymous) translation of Goethe. Callcott was also greatly affected by visual art, not altogether surprisingly since his brother, Sir Augustus Wall Callcott RA, once a chorister at Westminster Abbey, was a master of Romantic landscape painting.

On occasion composers fretted at the limitations of the glee and attempted to plant it in new ground. John Marsh of Chichester composed an extensive, lighthearted piece, *The City Feast, or Man of True Taste*, for three voices (in the form of a minuet and gavotte), with string accompaniment. R. J. S. Stevens's *Bragela*, for two pianos and voices, is a work of sonata-movement stature, which enjoyed considerable popularity in the United States after its publication in New York.

It was during the last decade of the eighteenth century that the classical English glees—particularly those of Joseph Baildon, John Wall Callcott, John Danby, the Earl of Mornington, John Stafford Smith, Richard John Samuel Stevens, and Samuel Webbe the elder, as well as a few by expatriate musicians—established themselves in polite circles in some of the principal cities of the United States. Rayner Taylor, a former Chapel Royal chorister, had some influence in the matter; he emigrated in 1792, taking copies of his own glees with him and composing more after his arrival. Glees were first sung publicly in Philadelphia in 1792, in Charleston in 1794, in New York—where an Anacreontic Society was founded—in 1795. In Boston many cultivated amateurs had their own collections of glees, but these 'in essence, a reflowering of the madrigal' were doomed to disappear whenever the informality of the concert gave way to professionalism and star guest performers.[8]

In London also, the character of the glee was affected by its promotion by professional singers, in the first instance in 'Vocal Concerts' (which were in fact not entirely vocal) organized by Samuel Harrison and William Knyvett. Such performances, in which a new style was represented by Knyvett, enjoyed a variable popularity until the 1820s. Knyvett, master of ornamentation, was distinguished also by 'the brilliancy and sweetness of his voice, his intonation, and his chastity of manner [as well as] the assimilation of tone—the exact light and shade—the distinct articulation, combined with . . . uncommon accuracy both of words and notes.'[9] The decline of the professionally sung glee was ascribed by one writer in 1823 to the vanity of female singers:

> But now-a-days, your principal female singer seems to regard such music as beneath her notice. A glee, properly so called, places her too much upon a level with the other singers of it, and if she vouchsafe to lend her assistance in any composition of this kind, it must be in that mongrel thing—yclept a harmonized air.[10]

The integrity of the true glee was, however, protected by the societies newly formed in Oxford and Cambridge (with the active support of their respective Professors of Music, William Crotch and Charles Hague) and London, which were dedicated to the protection of the species. Concerning the formation of the new London organization, taking the place of the now defunct Graduate Meeting, Callcott reported:

> On Thursday evening [November 1797] the Concentores [Sodales] held their first meeting this season, at their room in [the Buffalo Tavern, Bloomsbury] Holborn. The Society consists of the principal part of the leading men in the musical profession & they meet for their own amusement to sing Madrigals, Glees, Cannons [*sic*], Catches &c. Mr Horsley & several others produced a number of new compositions. A Cannon [*sic*] was particularly noticed for

[8] H. Earle Johnson, *Musical Interludes in Boston 1795–1830* (New York, 1943), 76.

[9] *QMMR* (1819), 470.

[10] *QMMR* (1823), 16–17.

its uncommon modulation, from the major to the minor Harmony. The next Meeting Mr Bartleman will be President.[11]

The Concentores Sodales was the most professional of the societies dedicated to the encouragement of the glee. Its purposefulness is indicated by the tone of some of its resolutions:

That each member shall be capable of writing correct counterpoint, or of taking a part in any composition offered to him.

That the President of the day do produce some new composition to be performed, and that he have full power to appoint who shall perform them [*sic*].

That copies of such compositions as are desired do remain in the Society's possession. If none should be particularly requested, the choice be left to the composer.

That a book be published periodically from the productions of the Society.

The Concentores maintained links with the past through Stafford Smith, whose versatility did not diminish, and Samuel Webbe, whose energies remained inextinguishable. Among the new composers heredity played its part: William Linley's father was Thomas Linley of Bath; Samuel Webbe's son—also named Samuel—moved to Liverpool, there to encourage glee activity; and Robert Cooke was the son of Benjamin Cooke. The leader of the new school was William Horsley, friend and son-in-law of Callcott (whose works he edited). Horsley, a man of wide cultural interests, was a close friend of Mendelssohn, who regretted that glees, these 'purely English products . . . were unknown and unobtainable in Germany,' [12] a sentiment that gratified those to whom it was communicated. Presumably it was for the better instruction of German singers that Horsley wrote his four-part glee *An Celias Laub*.[13]

The Concentores Sodales lasted until 1847; its books were then transferred to Gresham College, its reserves of wine passed to its secretary at the time, Thomas Forbes Walmisley (son of Thomas Attwood Walmisley), and the balance of its funds were used for a piece of plate to present to William Horsley.

In Manchester, during the post-Napoleonic period, when the benefits of the Industrial Revolution were beginning to advance middle-class prosperity and political and cultural aspirations, two glee clubs were established. Between them the Amateur Glee and Catch Club (founded in 1822) and the Gentlemen's Glee Club (founded in 1830) incorporated all the best glee traditions of harmonious fellowship. The atmosphere of the former's gatherings are colourfully recalled by the entries in its minute books. The members met at each others' houses 'in alphabetical rotation' on Saturday nights during the winter months. Any member not present at the end of a meeting (absent, perhaps, because he was unable to sing his appointed part) was liable to a fine of half-a-crown. Supper 'consisted of cold beef and a tart only, [to] be served at ten o'clock precisely'. In supplementary rules adopted in 1829 it was determined that 'two glees, at least, shall be sung, every evening without instrumental accompaniments'. Fines of one shilling were to be imposed on the person in charge of the evening if he did not provide sufficient copies of music for the party present, and on any member who 'declin[ed] to perform any part appointed to him'. Fines were allocated towards the purchase and binding of music.

Credit for some reduction in sex discrimination, and the eventual translation of ladies from kitchen to music-room, belongs to a Mr Bagshaw, the author of the significant resolutions.

On 26 February 1833 it was agreed that 'the Lady of the house where the Club shall be held, shall be at liberty to introduce two Female friends to the Glee Club Room until half past nine o'clock'. Five years later, on 8 February 1838, it was accepted that 'at future meetings it be allowable that cold Roast Fowls may be introduced, at the option of the President of the Evening, in addition to the usual supper fare of Cold Beef'. Two weeks later,

The introduction of Ladies not only to the Music room but to the supper table of the Club having been productive of much gratification to the Members and their friends, and that such having been found on experience to be promotive of the art of Glee Singing and its more general introduction into Society, it has been unanimously resolved that the President of the Club for the Evening be authorised to introduce to the Club during the entire Meeting such number of Ladies as he may deem proper.

The Manchester Gentlemen's Glee Club, 'based on the London model' was founded in 1830. Here it was clearly understood that it was 'a pleasant fiction . . . that every member . . . should be [and was] capable of taking his share in the execution of the programmes'. Professional singers (including sopranos and contraltos, with the male alto also much in evidence) were engaged from the start. Choirboys were briefly introduced in 1850. Distinguished persons on occasion came from London to the meetings, and William Horsley (one of a number of honorary members) composed his glee *Sweet smile* for the members. The club offered prizes of five pounds for a 'serious' or a 'cheerful' glee. Among the well-known musicians to submit works in the first three years were Thomas Attwood Walmisley (1831), Henry Bishop and Vincent Novello (1832), and Samuel Sebastian Wesley (1833, 1834). Of these the most important—whose composer's name seems unduly to have influenced the judges—was Novello's *Old May Morning*. Alfred Novello published the piece together with a long excerpt from a Manchester newspaper. This stated that glees had been submitted from all over

[11] BL Add. MS 27693, fo. 5.

[12] W. H. Cummings, 'Historic Songs, Glees, and Part-Songs', Lecture II, in *International Loan Exhibition: Musical Instrument Catalogue* (1900), 82 [catalogue of an exhibition held at Crystal Palace, July–November 1900].

[13] BL Add. MS 38554, also R. L. de Pearsall, *Es war ein König in Thule*, Add. MS 38544.

the country, and that their quality 'exhibited a gratifying proof that this peculiarly English department of Musical Science, is extensively and successfully cultivated'. The glees were frequently rehearsed and 'well got up by the singers'. Afterwards they were sung to the committee appointed to adjudicate in the matter 'at five successive meetings, which were held for the purpose'.

In the dedication (to Lord Burghersh, an amateur composer and founder of the Royal Academy of Music) of his *Six English Glees . . . including the Glee which gained the Prize given by the Manchester Gentlemen's Glee Club . . . and then performed at The Concentores Society, London (1832)* Bishop paid tribute to his own teacher, Francesco Biancho, 'that great Master of Contrapunto', though he showed no great capacity for demonstrating any skill of his own in that area. Bishop's talent was theatrical. His so-called glees (several hundred) include athletic pieces with soprano lines à la Rossini (*Now tramp o'er moor and fell*) and low-grade *Sturm und Drang* (*Now by day's retiring lamp*). The glee tradition nevertheless influenced Bishop's operatic choruses, but even more those of Arthur Sullivan.

In 1814 William Hawes, then Master of the Children of the Chapel Royal, and the composer of many glees, began publishing, and with his issue of an edition of *The Triumphs of Oriana* began a movement whose influence is not even yet exhausted. Thereafter the difference between glee and madrigal became increasingly blurred. Like the Bach revival in Germany the madrigal revival in England was a force of which the forward-looking composer could not remain unaware. The original Madrigal Society (founded in 1741) was still in existence and new societies for the cultivation of this form of music were established. Of these the first was in Bristol, founded in 1837 as a consequence both of lectures by Edward Taylor and of the inspiration of R. L. de Pearsall. In Manchester, in 1840, a split in the ranks of the Glee Club took place. Some 'admirers of the older and less sprightly but not less beautiful form of polyphonic music' felt that a society devoted exclusively to the cause of the madrigal should be set up. It was and the first director was the notable local glee composer William Shore.

By this time, however, choral societies were being founded with fresh intentions, to sing not only the best-loved of Handel's oratorios, but also those of Haydn and Mendelssohn, and of almost all the British (and some German) contemporary composers. Where the glee club continued, the original intention of sociability was retained, but the musical function became more general.

At the beginning of the nineteenth century there were three glee clubs in Worcester—the Worcester Glee Club itself (founded in 1810), and those founded slightly later and meeting respectively at the Crown and Unicorn hotels. Throughout his life Edward Elgar was associated with all of these (male-dominated) societies. He appreciated their conviviality, as well as his own early opportunity to play in instrumental groups rather than to listen to vocal ensembles. One work by Elgar is a gentle reflection on the tradition of the glee and, particularly, the Worcester Glee Club—*The Fountain*, to a poem by Henry Vaughan, composed in 1913. A feature of this little work is the singularly coloured harmonic passage—to the words 'thus fed my eyes, But all the earth lay hush'—which is suffused with the romantic atmosphere of the finest glees of the old school. Elgar dedicated this piece to an old friend, W. Mann Dyson, former secretary of the Worcester Glee Club and former cathedral lay clerk.

The last remains of the glee tradition appear in an otherwise undistinguished novel of the 1920s, *David of King's*, by E. F. Benson. Crowfoot is a Cambridge don of a 'highly sociable disposition', whose favourite hospitality is 'the glee-singing parties which he gave in his rooms after Hall every week'. A hilarious evening ends when the undergraduate singers are presented with the copies of Stevens's *Ye spotted snakes*.

> The spotted snakes proved to be teasers, and taxed the utmost talent of the company. The newts and blindworms did a lot of harm by not coming in right, and everyone got dreadfully muddled over 'Philomel with melody'. But Crowfoot by no means despaired of settling Philomel's hash at the next meeting, and offered copies all round for private practice.

Editorial Method and Performance

The aim of this collection is to show, as far as possible, the breadth of interest in the glee during the period in which it enjoyed supremacy in the field of part-singing. The selected works illustrate its relationship with literature, its social contexts, and its diversity of musical textures and expression.

Where such exists, a composer's autograph has been used. Otherwise authority—in differing degrees—resides in copies made with a composer's approval, copies that belonged to glee societies (also published pieces with particular dedications), and the most authoritative published versions. So far as texts are concerned, the versions used by the composers have been retained, despite discrepancies with the poets' originals. Capitalization and punctuation, often erratic, have been modernized.

The selected pieces range from three to five parts. In some cases texture may be adapted to the constitution of a particular ensemble. For example, where there are parts for two sopranos the lower part may be given to a light-voiced contralto, while parts for counter-tenor or male alto may (in the case of absence of such voices) be transferred to contralto. Clefs have been modernized (as was already recommended by some glee composers in the eighteenth century). For the greater comfort of singers it may on occasion be advantageous to transpose a work.

Sometimes glees were supported by keyboard accompaniment, despite the fact that until a relatively late stage none was suggested in either MS or printed score. Where a continuo part was provided, however, this has been realized, and independent accompaniments are given as they appear in the original sources.

In respect of ornamentation, John Wall Callcott (*A Musical Grammar*, ed. W. Horsley, 1817, 103–4) provided this guide: 'An appoggiatura . . . is a small note before a long one, from which it generally borrows half the value. Sometimes, however, the Appoggiatura is only one quarter of the note it precedes.' That it was thought judicious to exercise a degree of liberty, however, is illustrated by William Knyvett, alto singer and composer. In his day he was considered the perfect example of 'fine taste', demonstrated by 'the peculiar sweetness and minute delicacy of the compact but exquisite little ornaments which are from time to time most unexpectedly thrown in' (*QMMR*, 1819, 475).

Dynamics are sometimes stated, in broad terms, in original sources; sometimes they are not given. In the first case they have been modestly amplified in square brackets. In the second case an initial dynamic level is suggested, but expression is to be at the discretion of performers.

Manuscript sources

Bodleian Library, Oxford: nos. 10 (Tenbury 599), 21 (Tenbury 1324)

Boston (Mass.) Public Library, Allen A. Brown Collection, M. 430, 1–32: nos. 1, 11, 16–18, 25

British Library: nos. 12, 13 (Add. MS 31671)

Cambridge University Library: no. 4 (Add. MS 6645)

Chetham's Library, Manchester: no. 20 (Manchester Amateur Glee Club, from composer)

Gresham Collection, Guildhall Library, London: nos. 15, 27 (G Mus. 361)

Royal College of Music, London: nos. 6 (813, 814), 7 (722, 817), 8 (818)

The editor wishes to acknowledge the kind assistance of the libraries listed above, together with Hereford Cathedral Library, Manchester Central Library, Worcester Cathedral Library, and the University of Birmingham.

Published sources

no. 2: J. Battishill, *Collection of Songs* (*c.*1775)
no. 3: T. Welch & W. Hawes (*c.*1820)
no. 5: J. W. Callcott, *Collection of Glees* (1824)
no. 9: J. Corfe, *Twelve Glees II* (1791)
no. 14: W. Horsley, *Fourth Collection of Glees* (1827)
no. 19: Preston & Son (*c.*1794)
no. 22: *Amusement for Ladies VIII* (1793), no. 3
no. 23: R. Spofforth, *Set of Six Glees* (*c.*1796)
no. 24: *Eight Glees for Ladies* (1793)
no. 26: Royal Harmonic Institution (*c.*1826) (ded. St Cecilia Society, Birmingham)

PERCY M. YOUNG
University of Birmingham, 1989

1. The Love Rapture

ANON.

THOMAS AUGUSTINE ARNE
(1710–78)

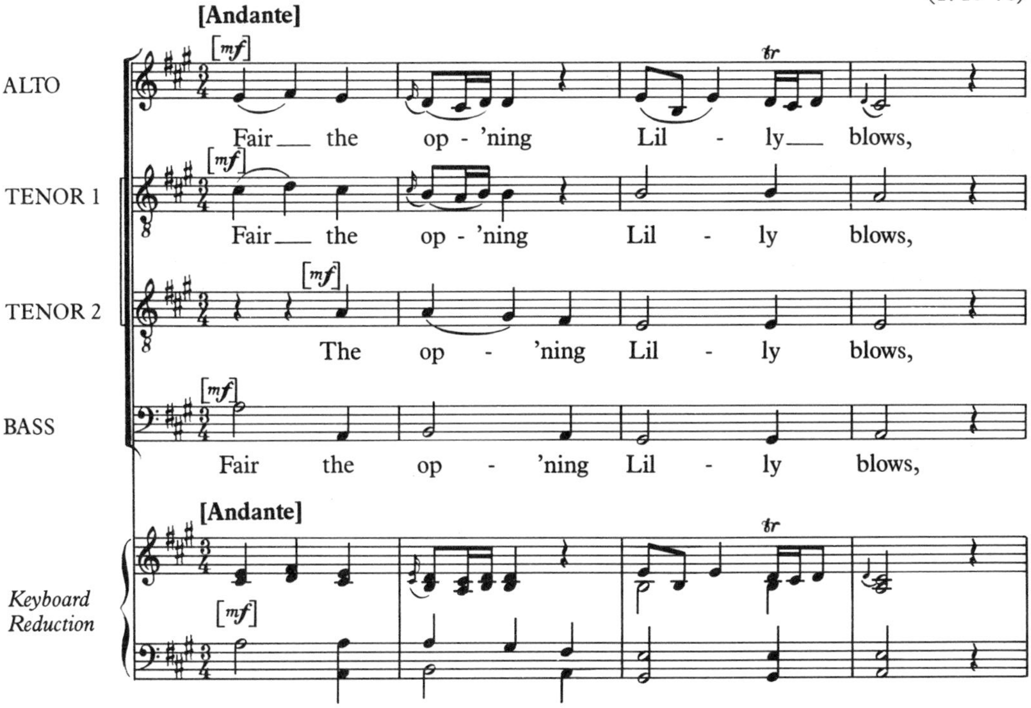

[Andante]

ALTO [mf] Fair the op - 'ning Lil - ly blows,

TENOR 1 [mf] Fair the op - 'ning Lil - ly blows,

TENOR 2 [mf] The op - 'ning Lil - ly blows,

BASS [mf] Fair the op - 'ning Lil - ly blows,

[Andante]

Keyboard Reduction [mf]

Printed in Great Britain
OXFORD UNIVERSITY PRESS, MUSIC DEPARTMENT, WALTON STREET, OXFORD OX2 6DP

9
f
Which per - fumes the
poco f
f
Which per - fumes, per - fumes the
p cresc.
f
Which per - fumes the Grove, per - fumes the
f
- fumes, per - fumes the Grove, per - fumes the
9
f
13
p
east - ern Grove, the fra - grant Cit - ron
p
east - ern Grove, Sweet the Cit - ron
p
east - ern Grove, Sweet the fra - grant Cit - ron
p
east - ern Grove, Sweet the fra - grant, the fra - grant Cit - ron
13
p

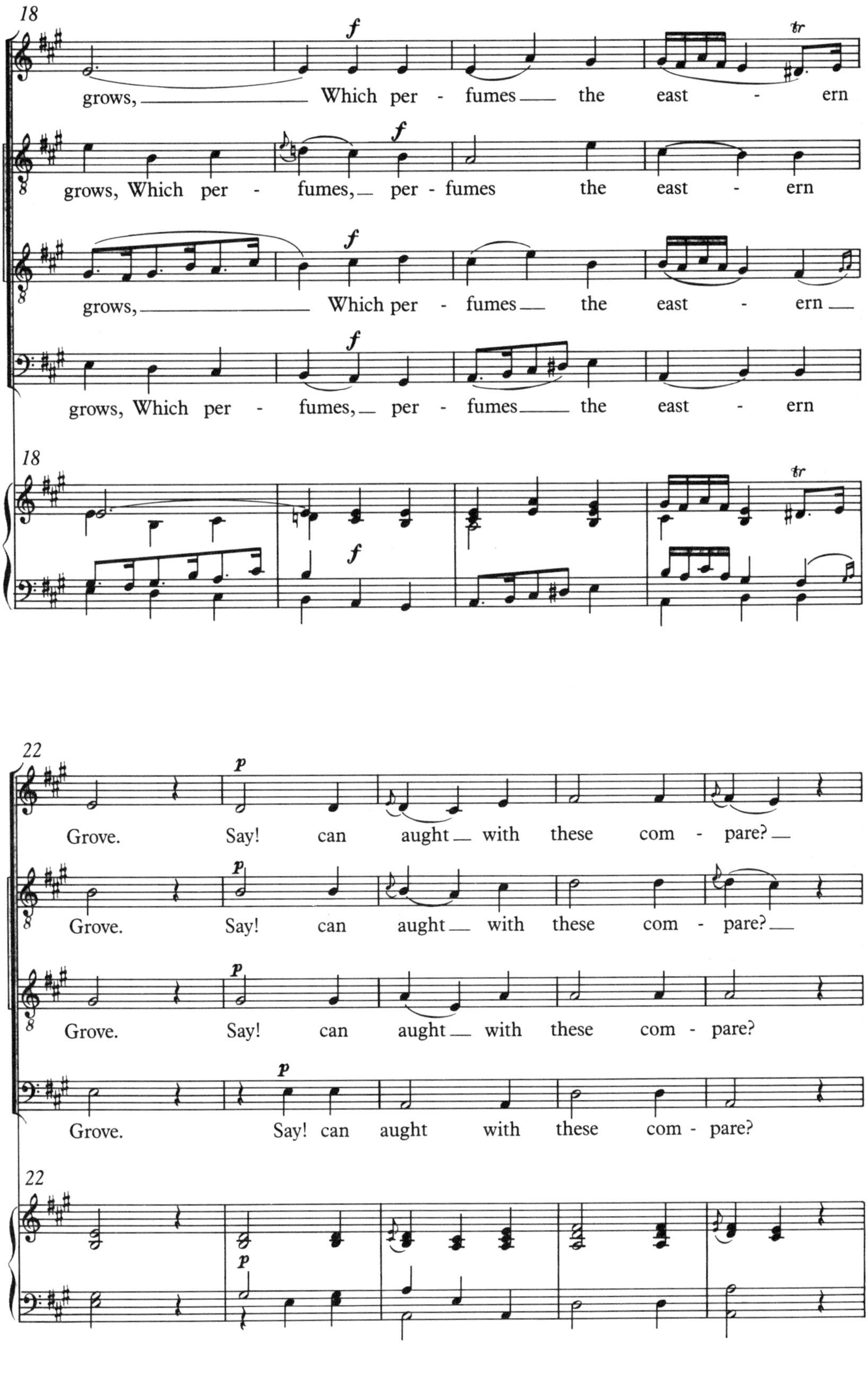

18

f *tr*

grows, Which per - fumes the east - ern

f

grows, Which per - fumes, per - fumes the east - ern

f

grows, Which per - fumes the east - ern

f

grows, Which per - fumes, per - fumes the east - ern

18

f *tr*

27
Say! can aught with these com - pare?
Say! can aught with these com - pare? Oh! much
Say! can aught with these com - pare? Oh! much
Say! can aught with these com - pare? Oh! much
27
32
Oh! much fair - er,
fair - er, oh! much fair - er, sweet - er
fair - er, oh! much fair - er, sweet - er
fair - er, oh! much fair - er, sweet - er
32

36
sweet - er far, Bloom the Charms of
far, sweet - er far, Bloom, bloom the Charms of
far, sweet - er far, Bloom the Charms, bloom the Charms of
far, sweet - er far, Bloom the Charms of
36

41
her I love. Say! can aught
her I love. Say! can aught with
her I love. Say! can aught with
her I love. Say! can aught with
41

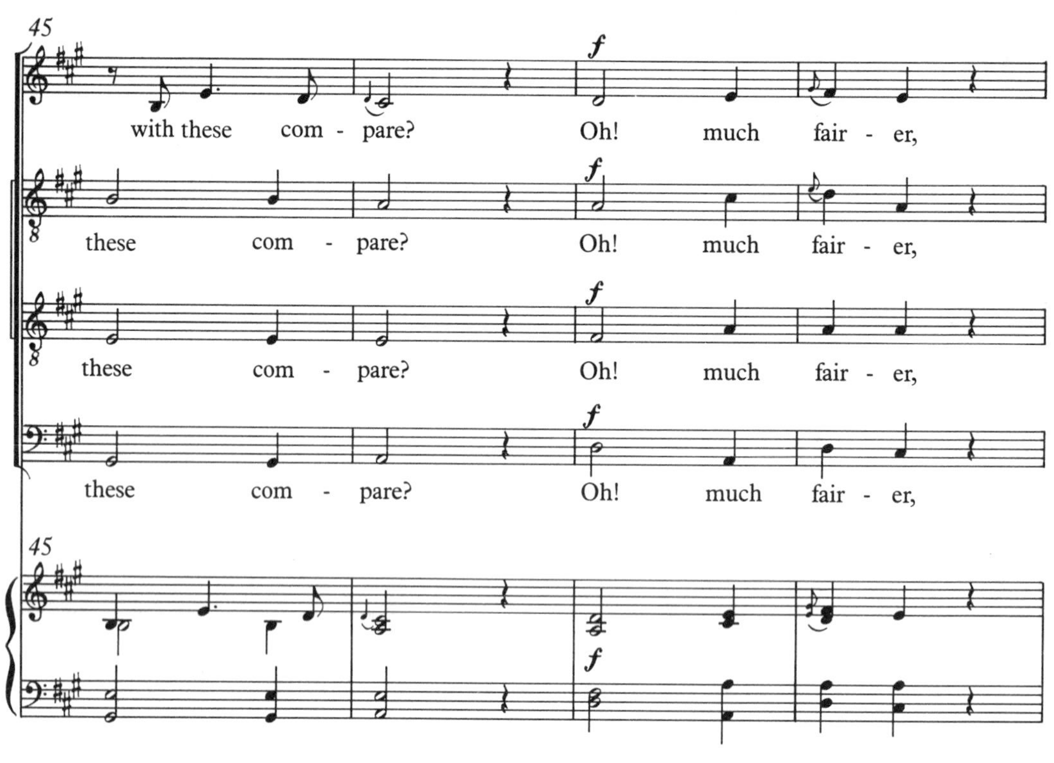
45
f
with these com - pare?
Oh! much fair - er,
these com - pare?
Oh! much fair - er,
these com - pare?
Oh! much fair - er,
these com - pare?
Oh! much fair - er,
45

49
p
f
sweet - er far,
Bloom the Charms
sweet - er far,
Bloom the Charms of
sweet - er far, Bloom the Charms, bloom the Charms of
sweet - er far, Bloom the Charms, the Charms of
49

53
p
of her I love. Oh! much fair - er, sweet - er
her I love. Oh! much fair - er, sweet - er
her I love. Oh! much fair - er, sweet - er
her I love. Oh! much fair - er, sweet-er
53
58
f
tr
far, Bloom the Charms of her I love.
far, Bloom the Charms of her I love.
far, Bloom the Charms of her I love.
far, Bloom the Charms of her I love.
58

2. Death's Final Conquest

JAMES SHIRLEY
(1596–1666)

JONATHAN BATTISHILL
(1738–1801)

10
p
ar - mour 'gainst our fate, Death lays his
ar - mour 'gainst our fate, Death lays his
ar - mour 'gainst our fate, Death lays his
ar - mour 'gainst our fate, Death lays his
10
p

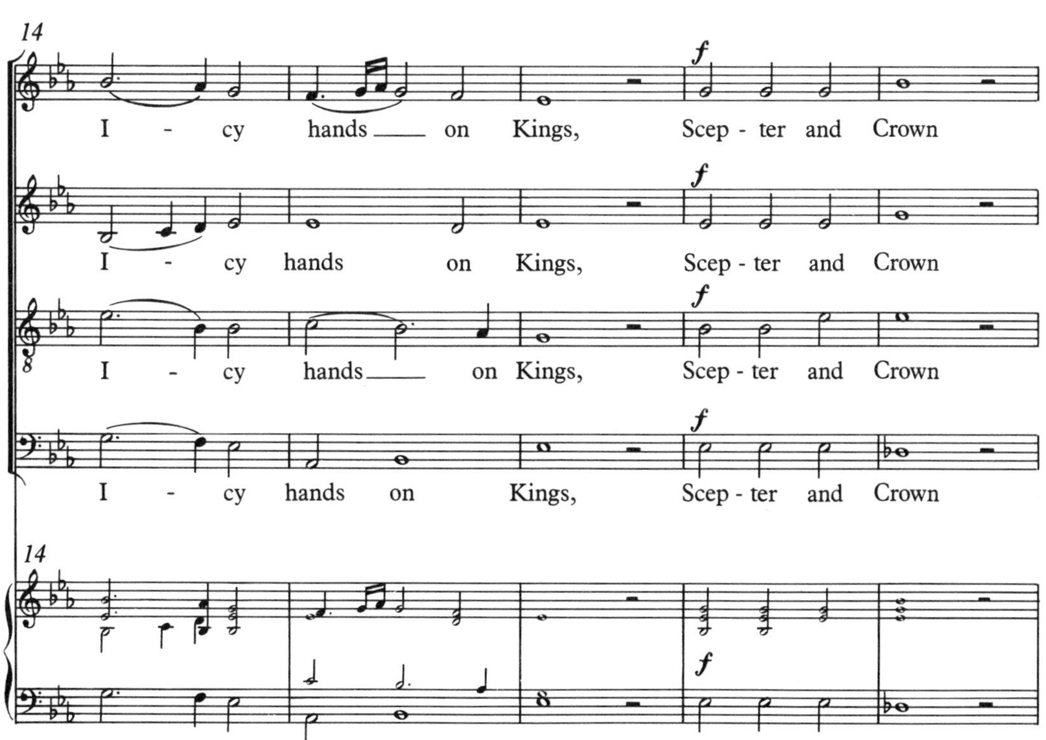
14
f
I - cy hands on Kings, Scep - ter and Crown
I - cy hands on Kings, Scep - ter and Crown
I - cy hands on Kings, Scep - ter and Crown
I - cy hands on Kings, Scep - ter and Crown
14
f

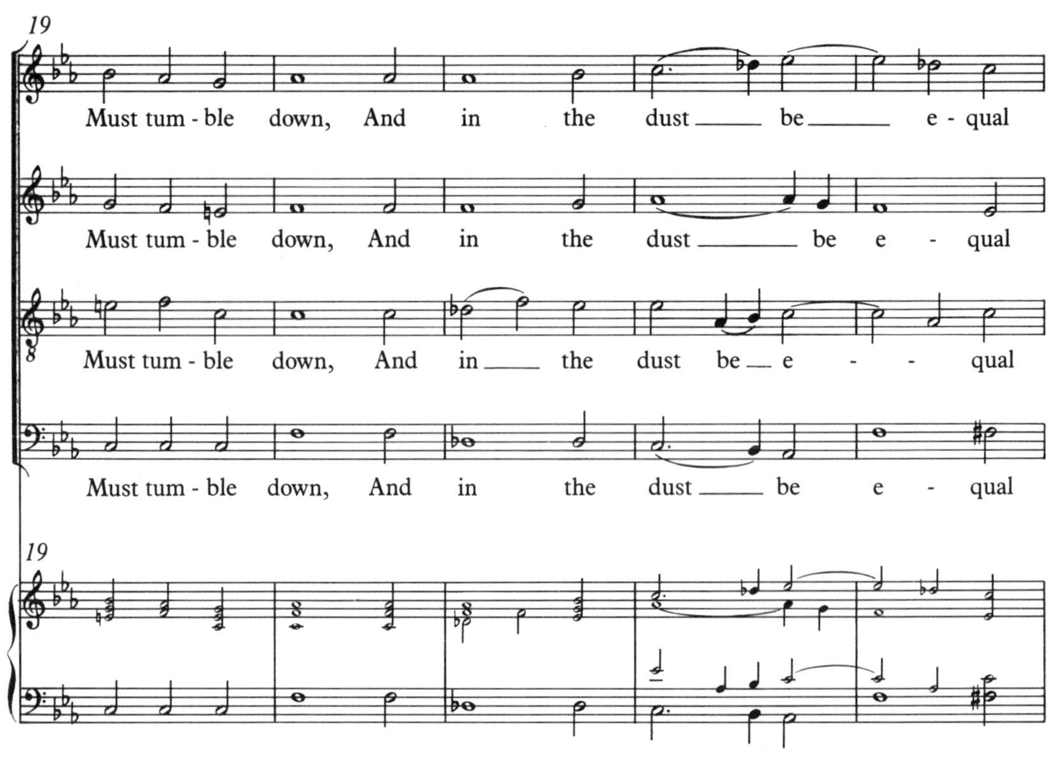
19
Must tum - ble down, And in the dust be e - qual
Must tum - ble down, And in the dust be e - qual
Must tum - ble down, And in the dust be e - qual
Must tum - ble down, And in the dust be e - qual
19

24
p
made, With the poor, poor crook - ed Scythe and
made, With the poor, the poor crook - ed Scythe and
made, With the poor, poor crook - ed Scythe and
made, With the poor, poor crook - ed Scythe and
24
p

28
Spade. Some Men with Swords may reap the Field, And
Spade. Some Men with Swords may reap the Field, And
Spade. Some Men with Swords may reap the Field, And
Spade. Some Men with Swords may reap the Field, And
28

33
plant fresh Lau - rels where they kill, But their strong
plant fresh Lau - rels where they kill, But their strong nerves
plant fresh Lau - rels where they kill, But their strong
plant fresh Lau - rels where they kill, But their strong
33

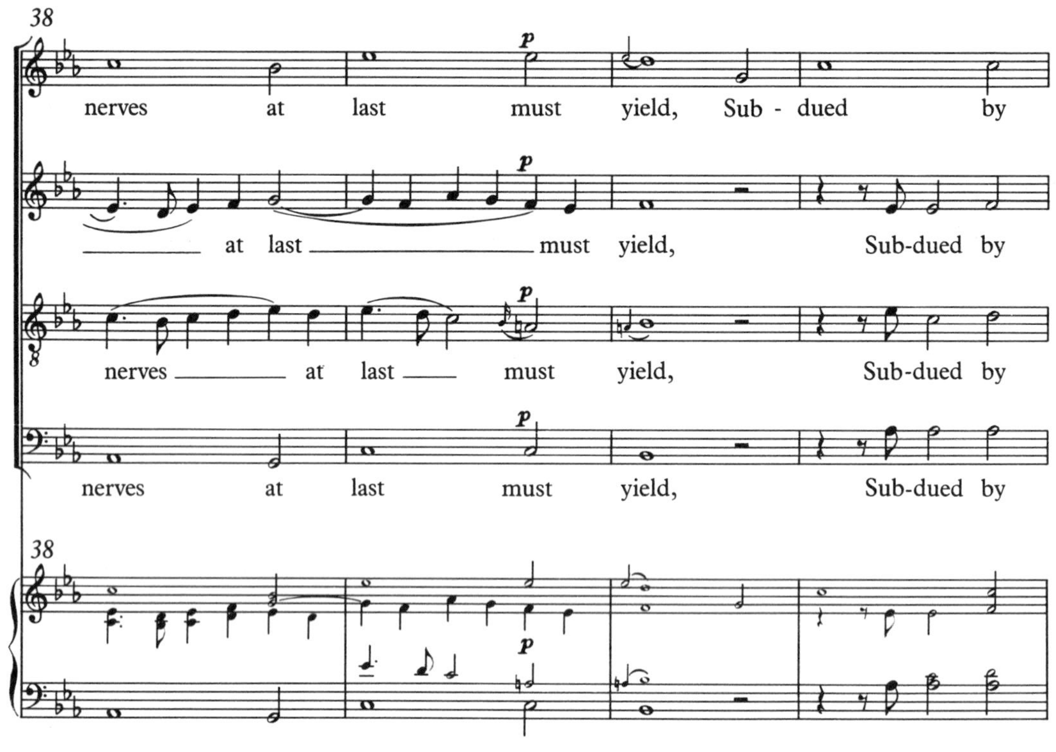
38
p
nerves at last must yield, Sub - dued by
at last must yield, Sub-dued by
nerves at last must yield, Sub-dued by
nerves at last must yield, Sub-dued by
38

42
f
p
one a - no - ther still; Ear - ly or late They
one a - no - ther still; Ear - ly or late They
one a - no - ther still; Ear - ly or late
one a - no - ther still; Ear - ly or late
42

47
stoop to fate, And must give up their mur - m'ring
stoop to fate, And must give up their mur - m'ring
They stoop to fate, And must give up their mur - m'ring
They stoop to fate, And must give up their mur - m'ring
47

52
breath When they, pale Cap - tives, creep to
breath When they, pale Cap - tives, creep to
breath When they, pale Cap - tives, creep to
breath When they, pale Cap - tives, creep to
52

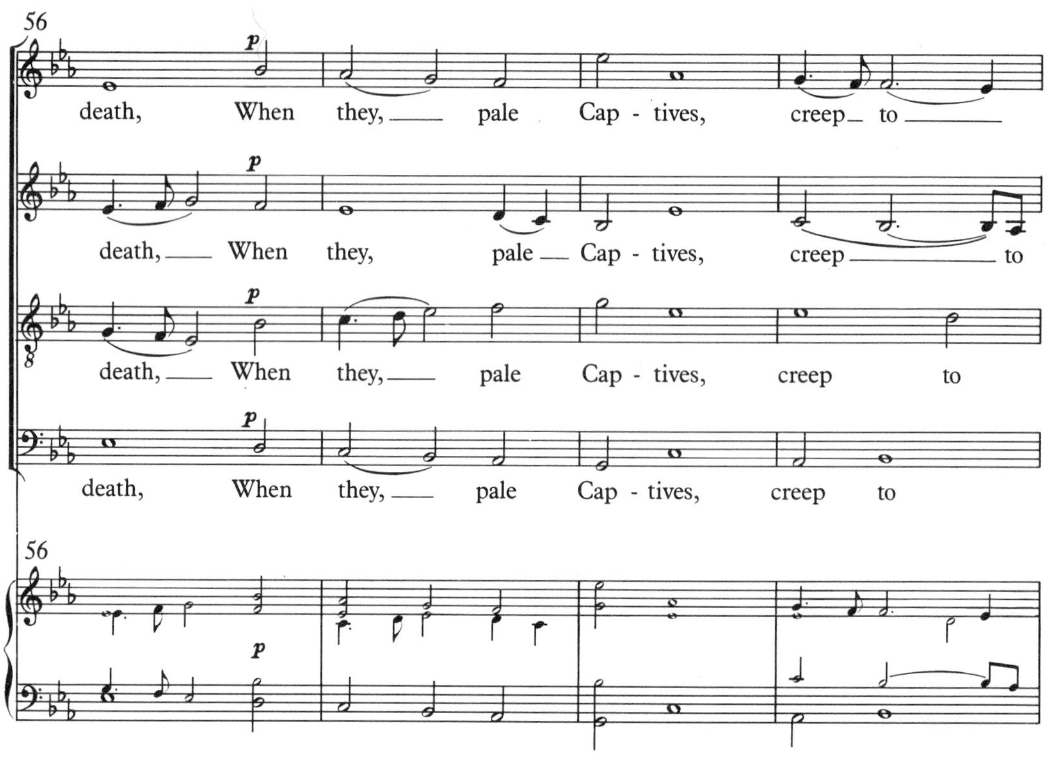
56
p
death, When they, pale Cap - tives, creep to
death, When they, pale Cap - tives, creep to
death, When they, pale Cap - tives, creep to
death, When they, pale Cap - tives, creep to
56
p

60
f
death. The gar - lands with - er on your brow, Then
death. The gar - lands with - er on your brow, Then
death. The gar - lands with - er on your brow, Then
death. The gar - lands with - er on your brow, Then
60
f

65
boast no more your might - y deeds; Up - on Death's
boast no more your might - y deeds; Up - on Death's pur -
boast no more your might - y deeds; Up - on Death's
boast no more your might - y deeds; Up - on Death's
65

70
pur - ple al - tar now See where the
-ple al - - tar now See where the
pur - ple al - tar now See where the
pur - ple al - tar now See where the
70

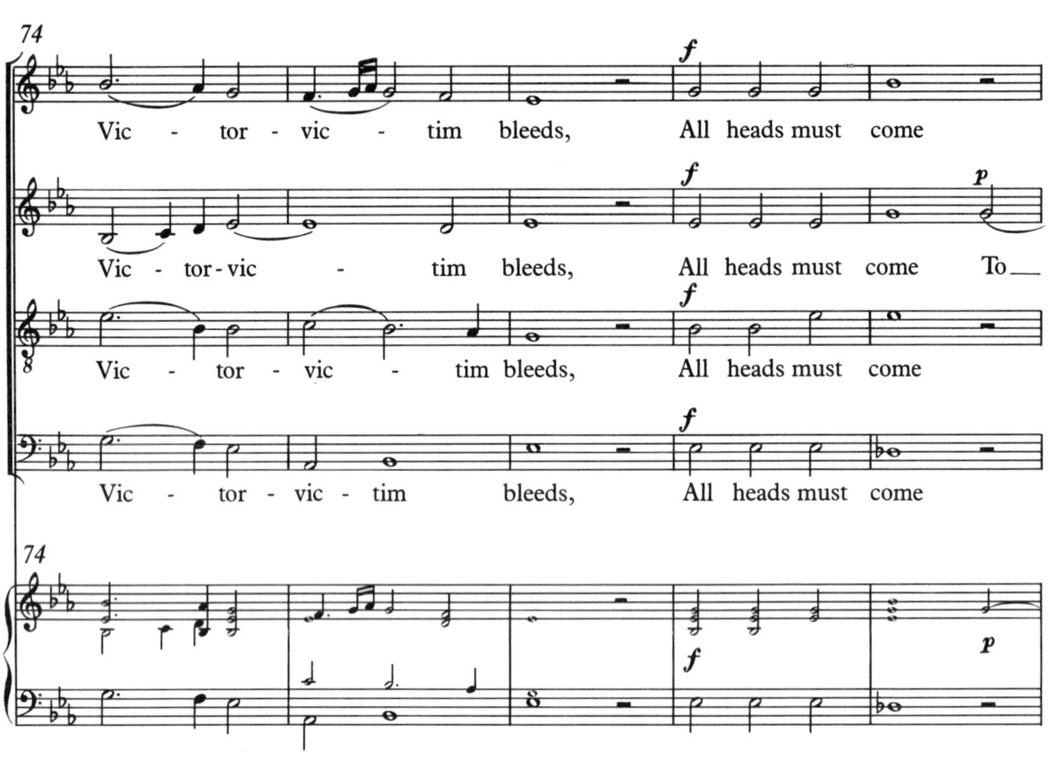
74
f
p
Vic - tor - vic - tim bleeds, All heads must come
Vic - tor - vic - tim bleeds, All heads must come To
Vic - tor - vic - tim bleeds, All heads must come
Vic - tor - vic - tim bleeds, All heads must come
74

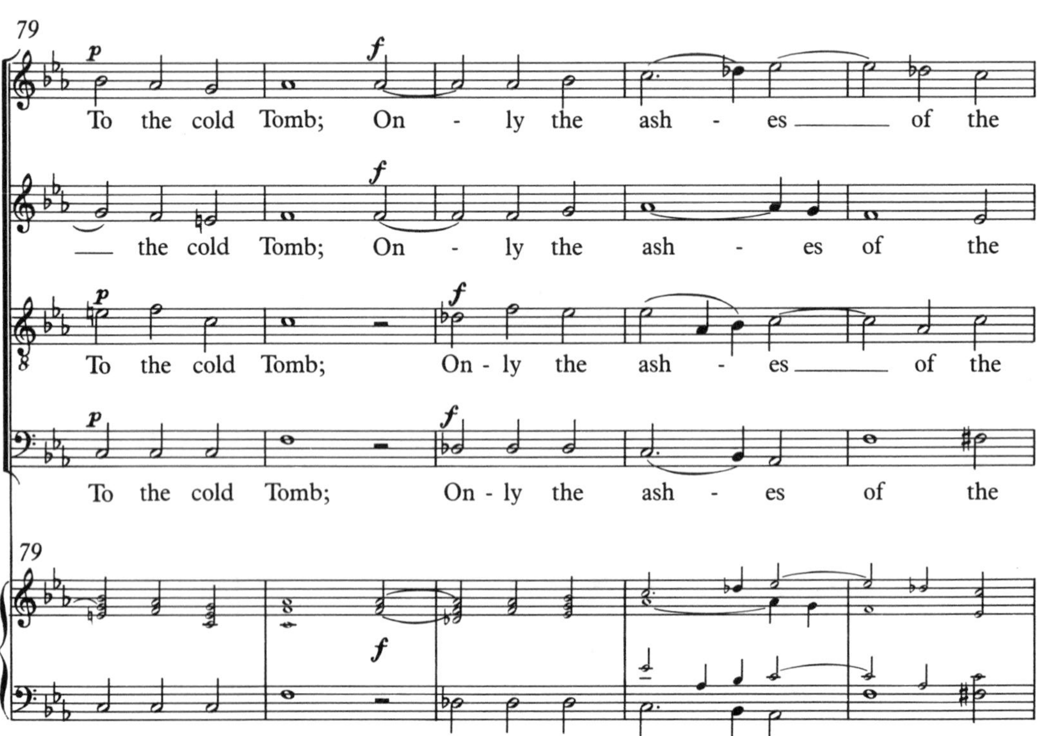
79
p
f
To the cold Tomb; On - ly the ash - es of the
the cold Tomb; On - ly the ash - es of the
To the cold Tomb; On - ly the ash - es of the
To the cold Tomb; On - ly the ash - es of the
79

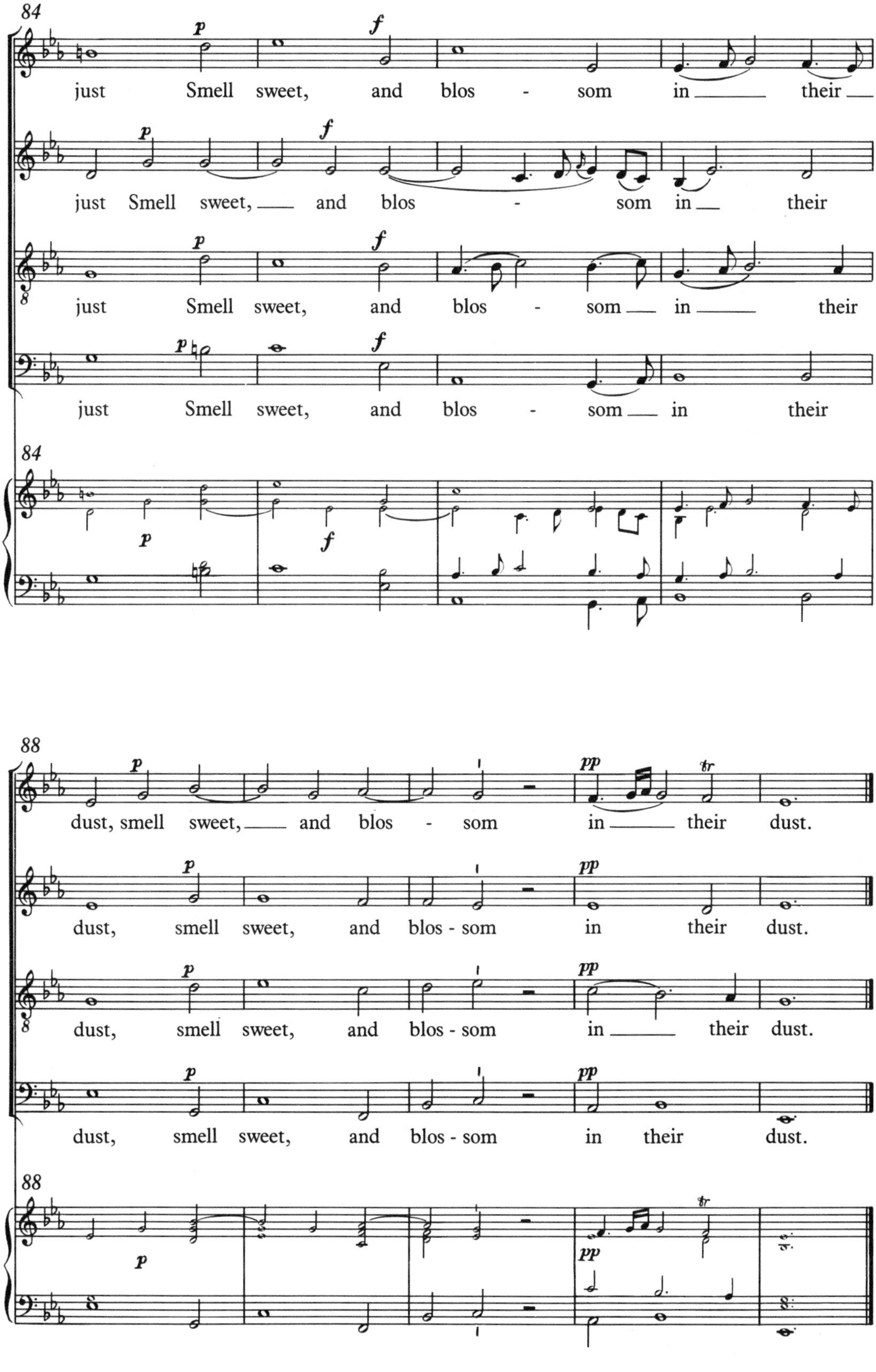

84

p *f*

just Smell sweet, and blos - som in their

just Smell sweet, and blos - som in their

just Smell sweet, and blos - som in their

just Smell sweet, and blos - som in their

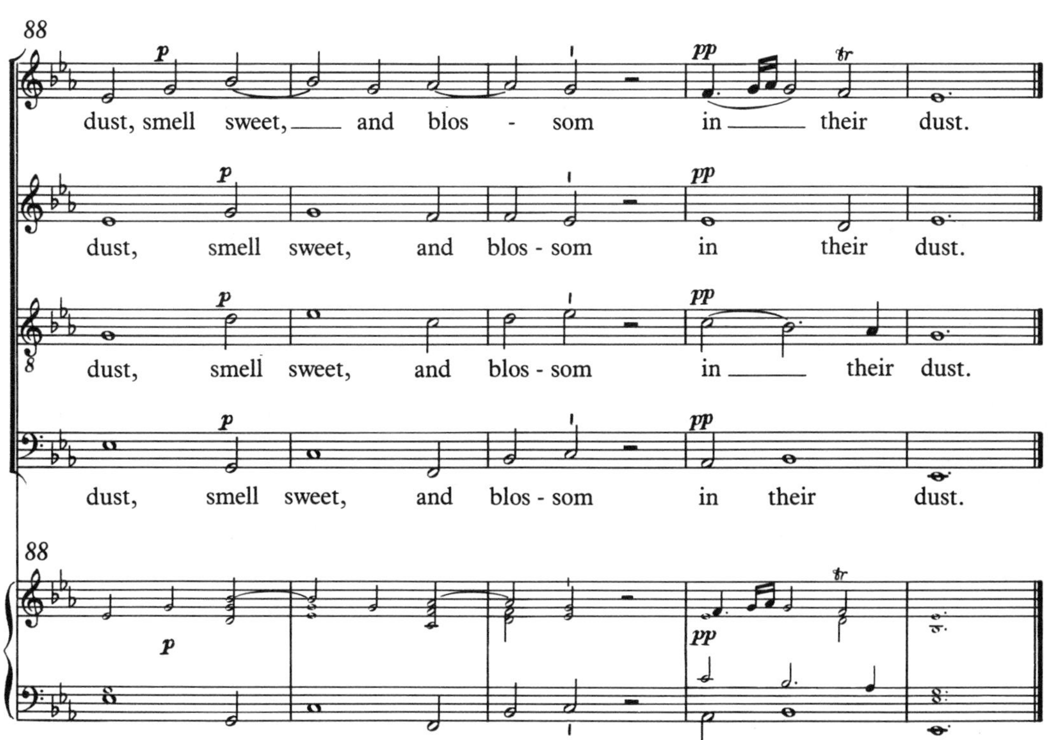

3. The Rose

ISAAC WATTS
(1674–1748)

JOHN BAYLEY
(1785–1833)

8
leaves are be - gin - ning to fade in an hour, And
are be - gin - ning to fade in an hour, And
leaves are be - gin - ning to fade in an hour, And
are be - gin - ning to fade in an hour, And
8

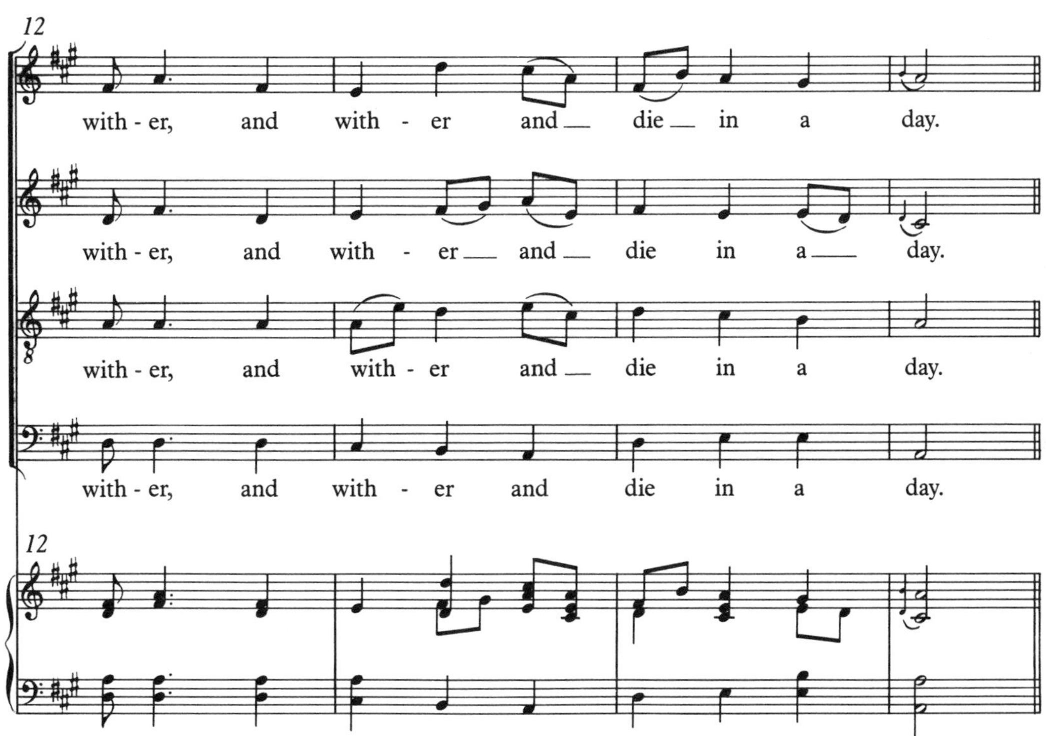
12
with - er, and with - er and die in a day.
with - er, and with - er and die in a day.
with - er, and with - er and die in a day.
with - er, and with - er and die in a day.
12

16
So frail is the youth and the beau - ty of
So frail is the youth and the beau - ty of
So frail is the youth and the beau - ty of
So frail is the youth and the beau - ty of
16

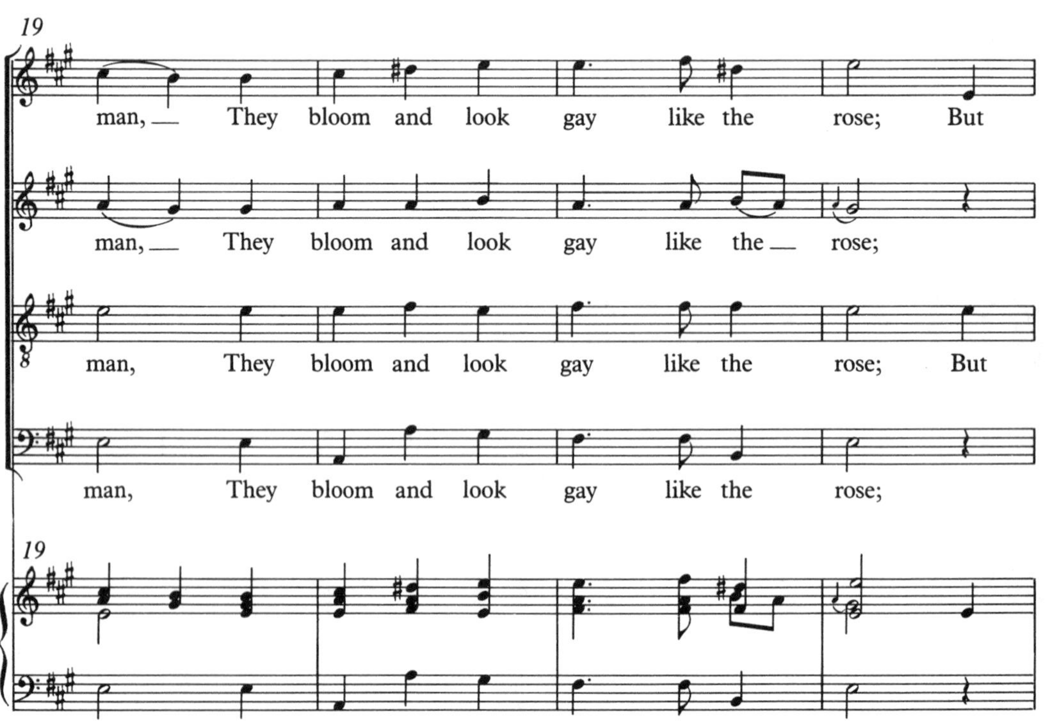
19
man, They bloom and look gay like the rose; But
man, They bloom and look gay like the rose;
man, They bloom and look gay like the rose; But
man, They bloom and look gay like the rose;
19

23

all our fond care to pre - serve them is vain, Time

our fond care to pre - serve them is vain, Time

all our fond care to pre - serve them is vain, Time

our fond care to pre - serve them is vain, Time

23

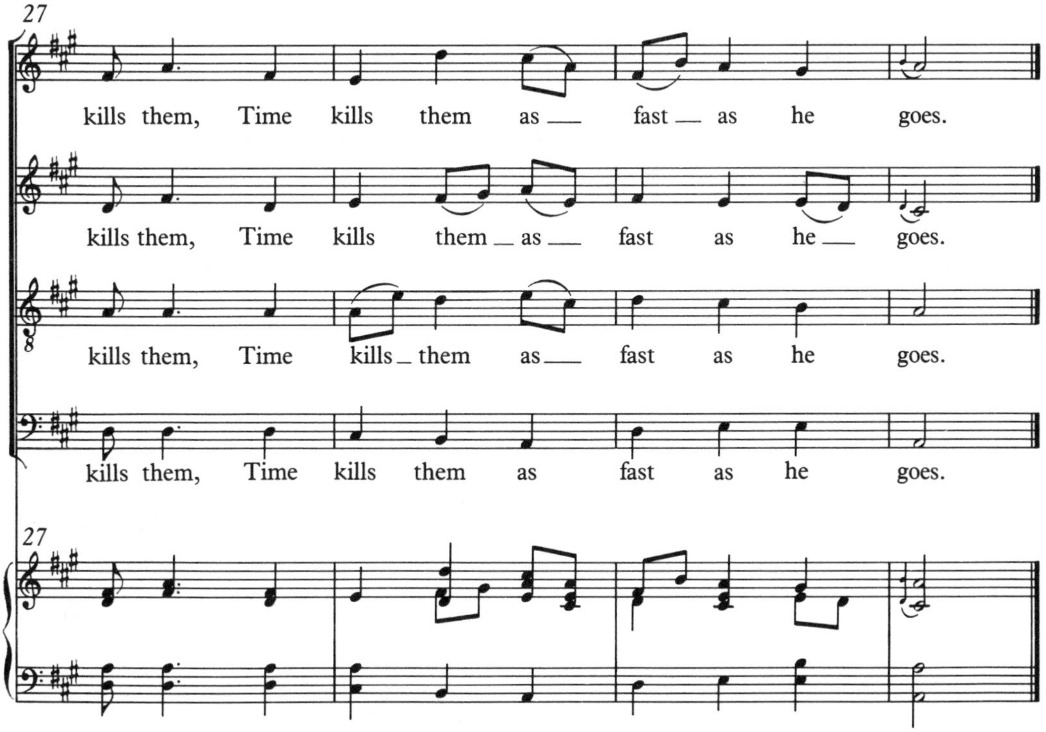

27

kills them, Time kills them as fast as he goes.

kills them, Time kills them as fast as he goes.

kills them, Time kills them as fast as he goes.

kills them, Time kills them as fast as he goes.

4. The poor soul sat sighing

SHAKESPEARE
(1564–1616)
(*Othello*, IV. iii)

JOHN CHRISTMAS BECKWITH
(1750–1809)

[Andante]

[*p*]

SOPRANO
The poor soul sat sigh - ing near a sy - ca-more

ALTO
The poor soul sat sigh - ing near a sy - ca-more

TENOR
The poor soul sat sigh - ing near a sy - ca-more

BASS
The poor soul sat sigh - ing near a sy - ca-more

[Andante]

Keyboard Accompaniment

[*p*]

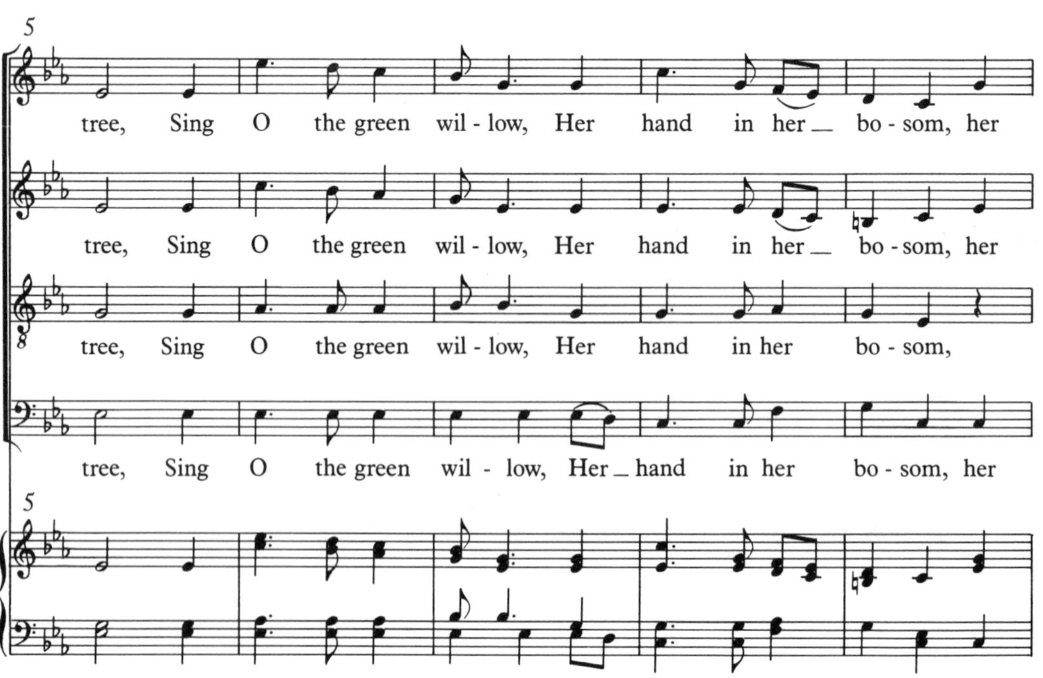

10
head on her knee, Sing O the green
head on her knee, Sing O the green wil - low, sing O the green
wil - low,
head on her knee, wil -
10
15
wil - low, sing O the green wil - low, the green wil-low tree.
wil - low, sing O the green wil - low, the green wil-low tree.
Sing O the green wil - low, the green wil-low tree.
- low, wil - low, the green wil-low tree.
15

20
The cold streams ran
The cold streams ran
The cold streams ran
The cold streams ran
20

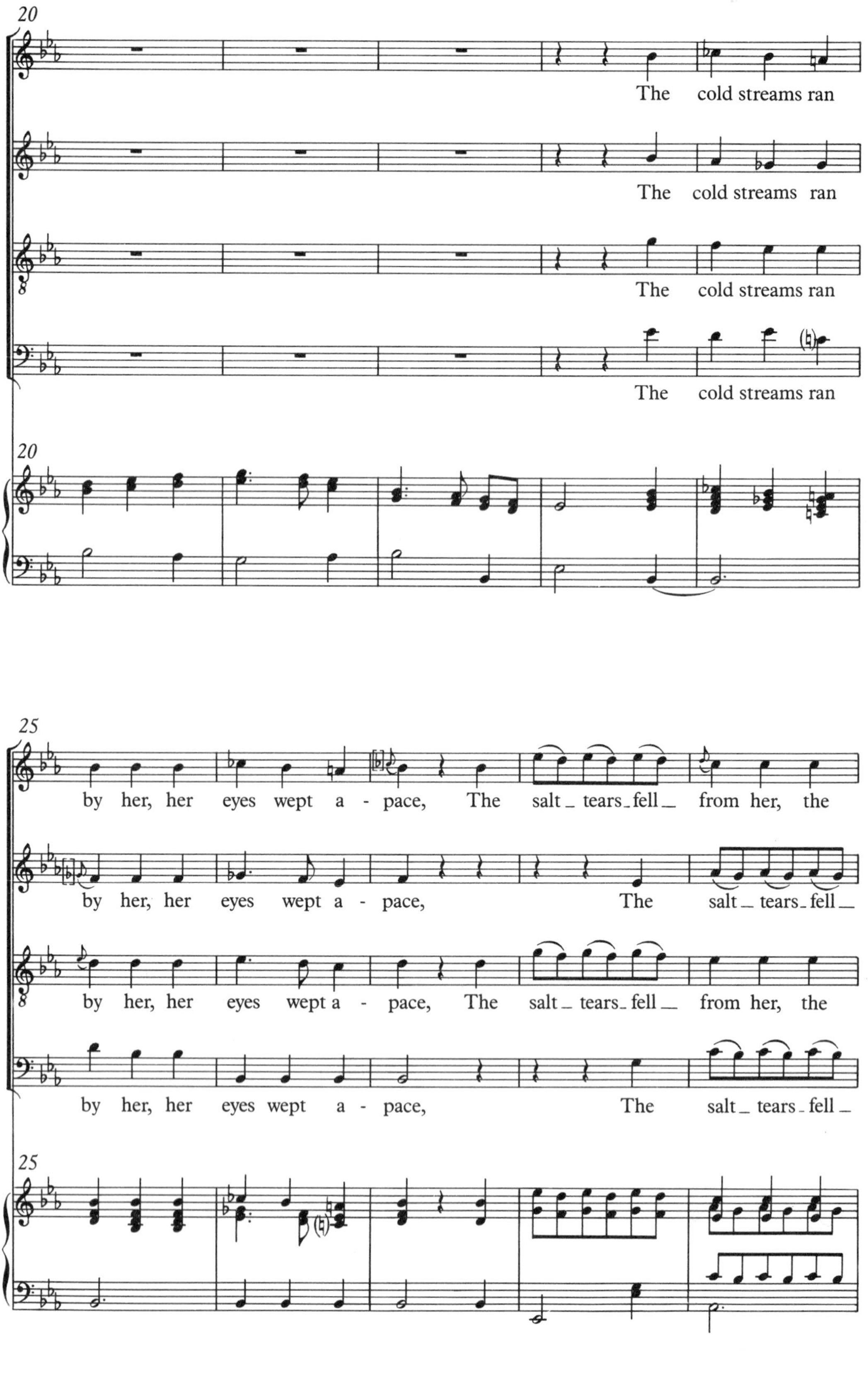

25

by her, her eyes wept a - pace, The salt _ tears _ fell _ from her, the

by her, her eyes wept a - pace, The salt _ tears _ fell _

by her, her eyes wept a - pace, The salt _ tears _ fell _ from her, the

by her, her eyes wept a - pace, The salt _ tears _ fell _

25

30
salt _ tears _ fell _ from her, the salt tears fell from her and
from her, the salt _ tears _ fell _ from her, fell from her and
salt _ tears _ fell _ from her, the salt tears fell from her and
from her, the salt _ tears _ fell _ from her, fell from her _ and
30
34
drown - ed her face.
drown - ed her face.
drown - ed her face.
drown - ed her face.
34

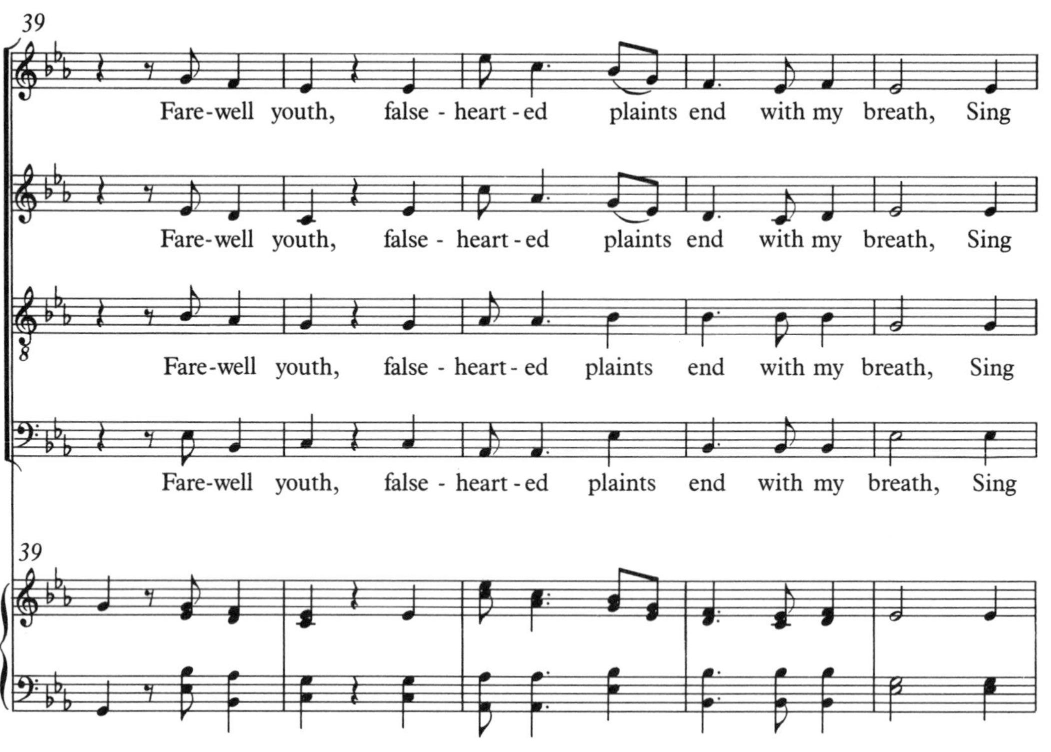
39
Fare-well youth, false - heart - ed plaints end with my breath, Sing
Fare-well youth, false - heart - ed plaints end with my breath, Sing
Fare-well youth, false - heart - ed plaints end with my breath, Sing
Fare-well youth, false - heart - ed plaints end with my breath, Sing
39

44
O the green wil - low, her hand in her — bo - som, her head on her
O the green wil-low, her hand in her — bo - som, her head on her
O the green wil-low, her hand in her bo - som,
O the green wil - low, her — hand in her bo - som, her head on her
44

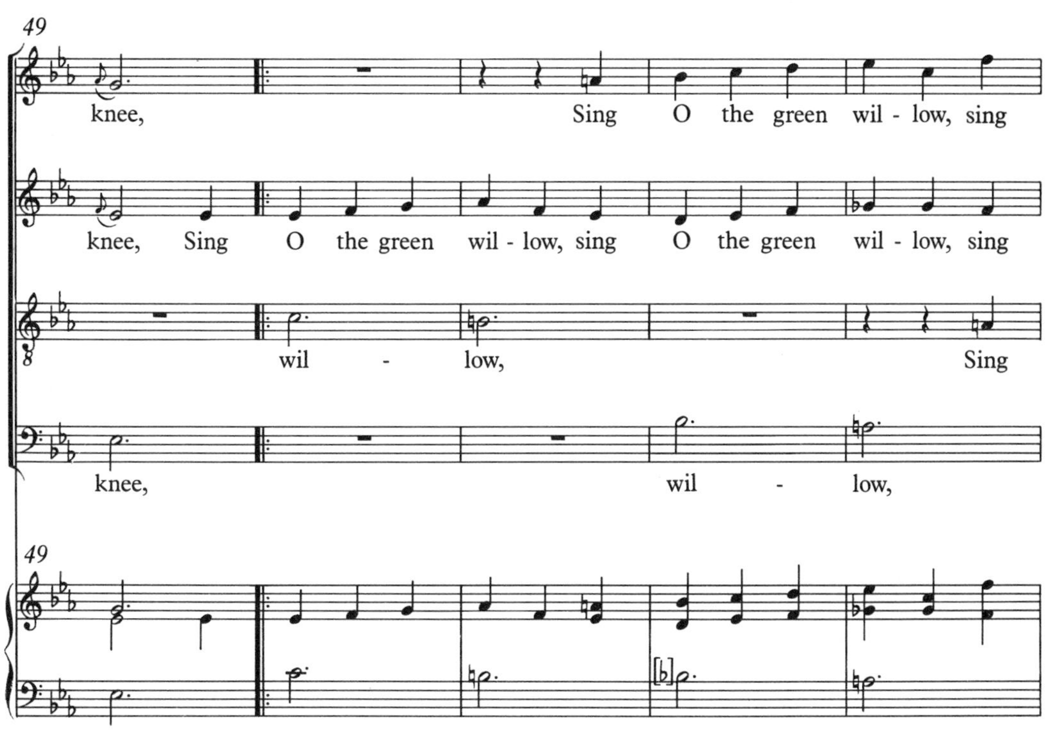
49
knee,
Sing O the green wil - low, sing
knee, Sing O the green wil - low, sing O the green wil - low, sing
wil - low,
Sing
knee,
wil - low,
49

54
1st time
2nd time
O the green wil - low, the green wil - low tree. tree.
O the green wil - low, the green wil - low tree. Sing tree.
O the green wil - low, the green wil - low tree. tree.
wil - low, the green wil - low tree. tree.
54
1st time
2nd time

5. Thyrsis, when he left me

THOMAS GRAY
(1716–71)

JOHN WALL CALLCOTT
(1766–1821)

Moderately (♩ = 112)

cresc.

SOPRANO *mf* Thyr - sis, when he left me, swore, In the

ALTO *mf* Thyr - sis, when he left me,

TENOR *mf* Thyr - sis, when he left me, *cresc.* swore,

BASS *mf* Thyr - sis, when he left me,

Moderately (♩ = 112)

Keyboard Reduction *mf* *cresc.*

9
- turn;
[mf]
swore, In the spring he would re - turn, in the
[mf]
- turn, he would re - turn; swore, In the spring, in the
[mf]
Thyr - sis, when he left me, swore, In the
9
[mf]
13
spring he would re - turn, in the spring he would re - turn;
spring he would re - turn, he would re - turn;
spring he would re - turn, in the spring he would re - turn;
13

17
Ah!
p
Ah! what means that op - 'ning flow'r,
p
Ah! what means that op - 'ning flow'r,
[p]
Ah! that op - 'ning flow'r,
17
p
21
espress.
Ah! And the
p
Ah! what means that op - 'ning flow'r,
p
Ah! what means that op - 'ning flow'r,
[p]
Ah! that op - 'ning flow'r,
21
p
espress.

25
cresc.
bud that decks the thorn? And the bud that decks the thorn? And the
cresc.
And the
cresc.
And the bud that decks the thorn? And the
cresc.
And the
25
cresc.
29
bud that decks the thorn?
dolce
bud that decks the thorn? 'Twas the night - in - gale that sung, 'twas the
dolce
bud that decks the thorn? 'Twas the night - in - gale that sung, 'twas the
bud that decks the thorn? 'Twas the
29
dolce

33

cresc.

'Twas the lark that up - ward _ sprung.

cresc.

lark that up - ward sprung, 'twas the lark that up - ward sprung.

cresc.

night - in - gale _ that _ sung, 'Twas the lark that up - ward sprung.

cresc.

night - in - gale that sung, 'Twas the lark that up - ward sprung.

33

cresc.

37

p

I - dle notes, un - time - ly green, _

I - dle notes,

p

I - dle notes, Why such

p

I - dle notes, un - time - ly green, Ah!

37

p

41
[p]
Why such un - a - vail - ing
un - a - vail - ing haste? Why such un - a - vail - ing
Why such un - a - vail - ing
41
44
Why such un - a - vail - ing haste? Why such un - a - vail - ing
haste?
haste? Why such un - a - vail - ing
haste? Why such un - a - vail - ing
44

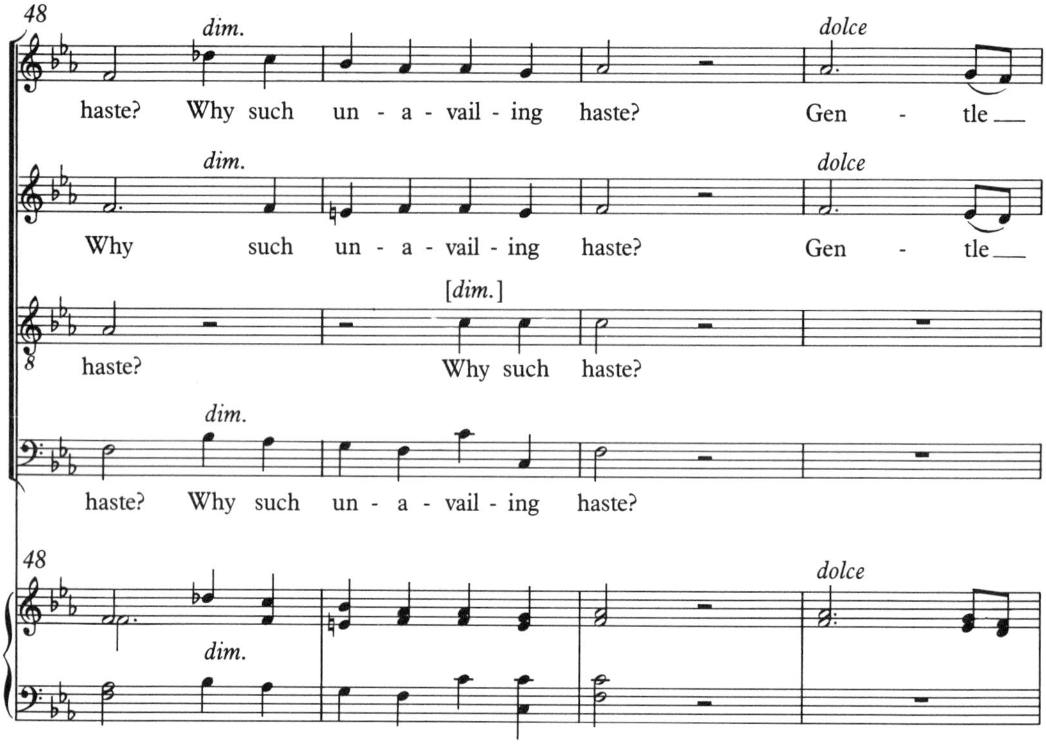

48

dim. *dolce*

haste? Why such un - a - vail - ing haste? Gen - tle —

dim. *dolce*

Why such un - a - vail - ing haste? Gen - tle —

[*dim.*]

haste? Why such haste?

dim.

haste? Why such un - a - vail - ing haste?

48

dolce

dim.

56
dolce
past; Gen - tle gales and skies se -
past; Gen - tle gales and skies se -
Gen - tle gales and skies se -
Gen - tle gales and skies se -
60
- rene, Prove not al - ways win - ter past; Cease my
- rene, Prove not al - ways win - ter past; Cease my
- rene, Prove not al - ways win - ter past; Cease my
- rene, Prove not al - ways win - ter past; Cease my

65
p
[pp]
doubts, my fears re - move, Spare the ho - nor
doubts, my fears re - move, Spare the ho - nor
doubts,
doubts, my fears re - move, Spare,
65
p
[pp]

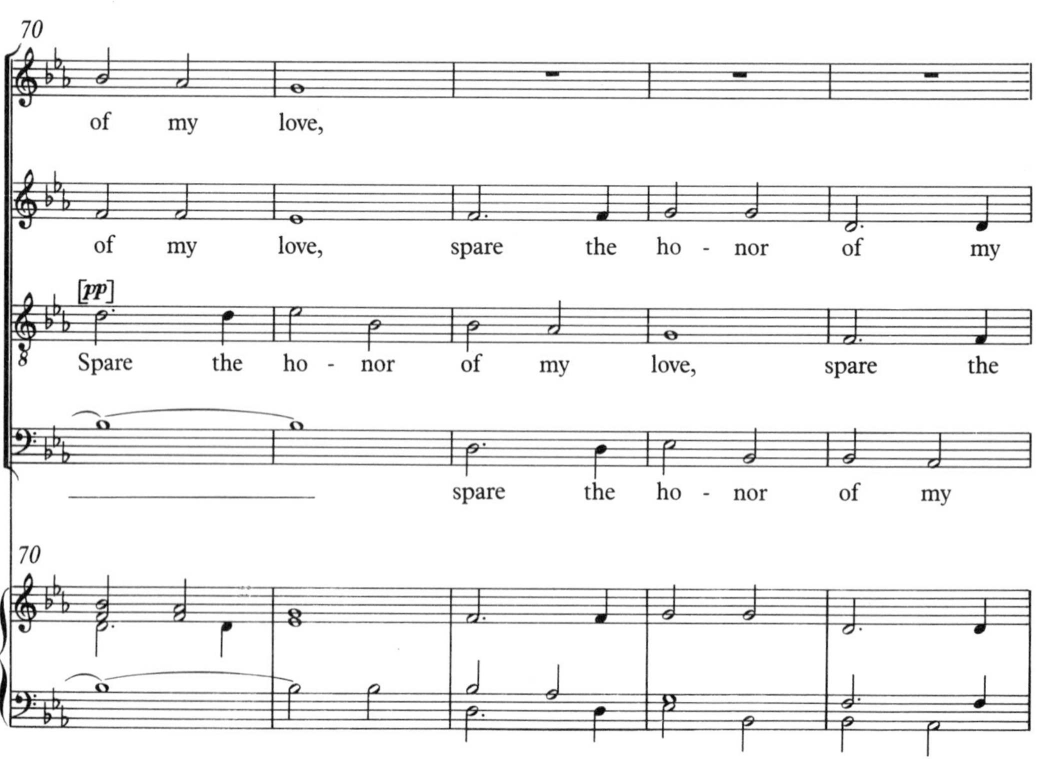
70
of my love,
of my love, spare the ho - nor of my
[pp]
Spare the ho - nor of my love, spare the
spare the ho - nor of my
70

75
[p] espress.
spare the ho - nor of my love, spare the ho - nor of my
love, O spare, spare, spare, spare,
ho - nor of my love, spare, spare,
love, O spare the ho - nor of my
79
cresc.
love, spare the ho - nor of my love, spare the ho- nor of my love.
spare the ho - nor of my love, spare the ho- nor of my love.
spare the ho - nor of my love, spare the ho- nor of my love.
love, spare the ho - nor of my love, spare the ho- nor of my love.

6. Hark, the Lark

SHAKESPEARE
(1564–1616)
(*Cymbeline*, II. iii)

BENJAMIN COOKE
(1734–93)

* Two versions of this piece exist: one in D without accompaniment (sent to the Catch Club); the other in B flat with a keyboard part. The latter is shown here, but the accompaniment can be omitted if desired.

7
loud
Lark at Heav-en's gate sings, and Phoe - bus 'gins a -
[loud]
Lark at Hea-ven's gate sings, and Phoe - bus 'gins a -
[loud]
Lark at Hea-ven's gate sings, and Phoe - bus 'gins a -
[loud]
Lark at Hea-ven's gate sings, and Phoe - bus 'gins a -
7
[loud]
10
- rise, His steeds to wa - ter at those
- rise, His steeds to wa - ter at those
- rise, His steeds to wa - ter at those springs On
- rise, His steeds to wa - ter at those
10

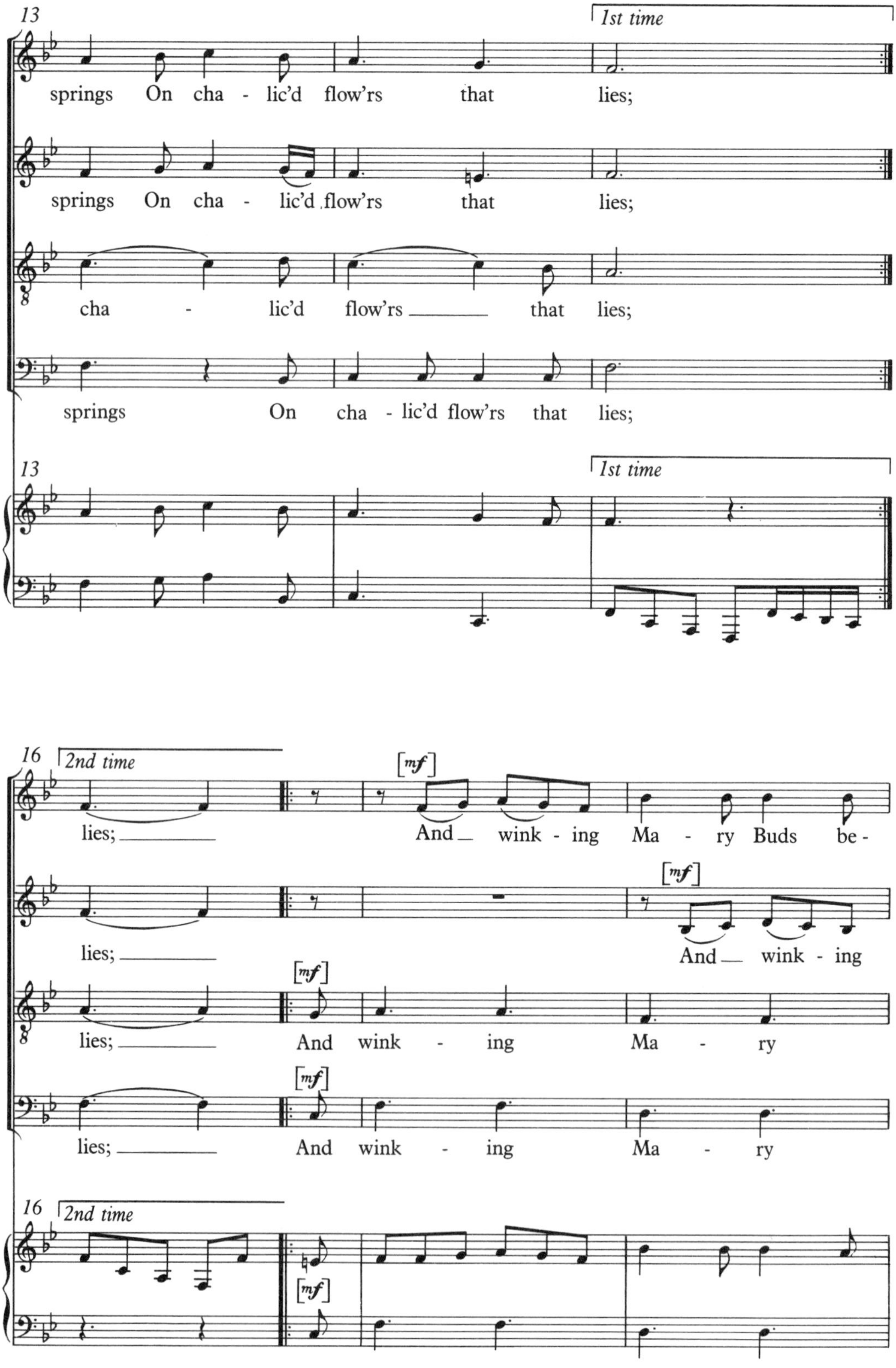

13

1st time

springs On cha - lic'd flow'rs that lies;

springs On cha - lic'd flow'rs that lies;

cha - lic'd flow'rs ___ that lies;

springs On cha - lic'd flow'rs that lies;

13

1st time

19
-gin To ope their gold - en eyes, And wink - ing
Ma - ry Buds be - gin To ope, wink - ing
Buds be - gin To ope, be -
Buds be - gin To ope, be -
19

22
Slow
Ma - ry Buds be - gin To ope their gold - en
Ma - ry Buds be - gin To ope their gold - en
-gin to ope their gold - en
-gin to ope their gold - en
22
Slow

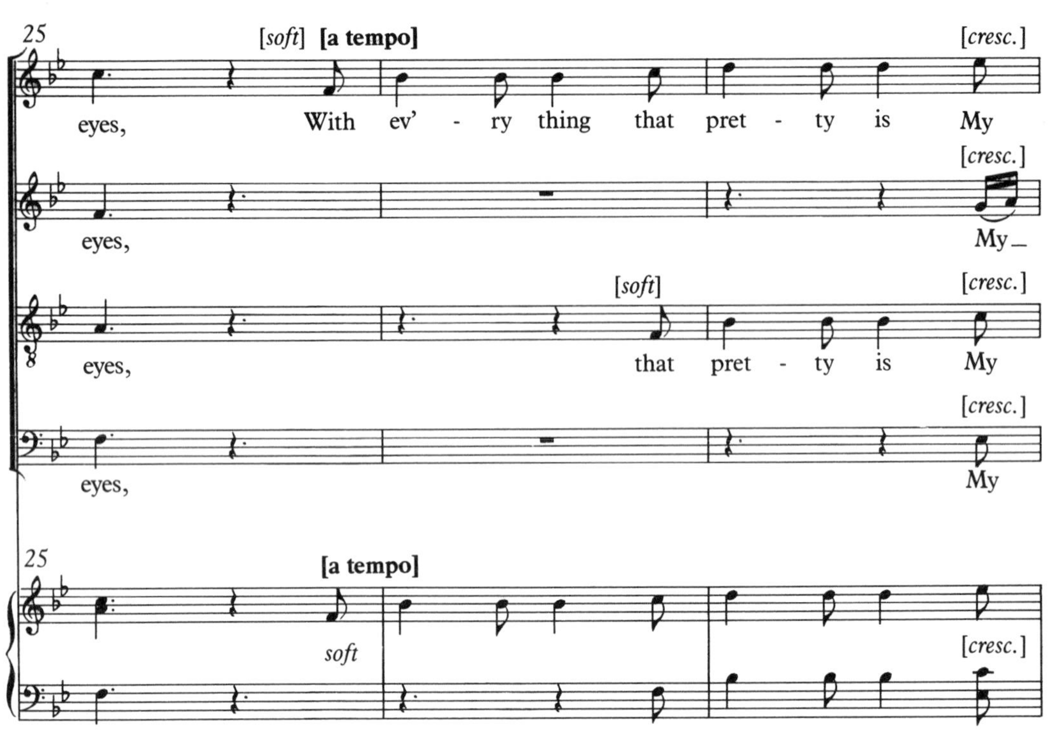

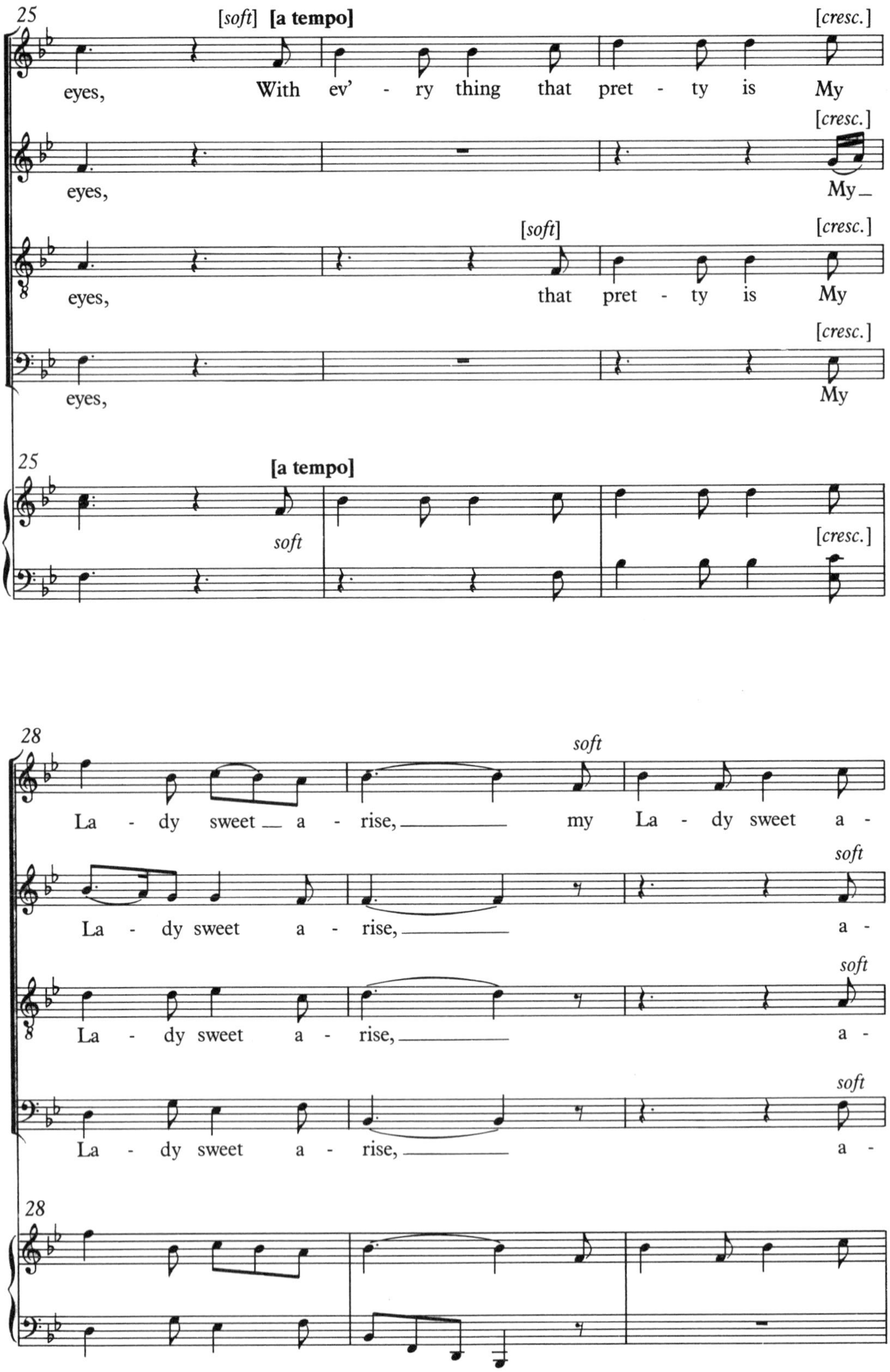

28

soft

La - dy sweet a - rise, my La - dy sweet a -

soft

La - dy sweet a - rise, a -

soft

La - dy sweet a - rise, a -

soft

La - dy sweet a - rise, a -

28

31
very soft
- rise, my La - dy sweet a - rise, With ev' - ry thing that
[very soft]
- rise, a - rise, With ev' - ry thing that
- rise, my La - dy sweet a - rise, With ev' - ry thing that
- rise, a - rise, With ev' - ry thing that
31
very soft

35
loud
pret - ty is My La - dy sweet a - rise, a -
[loud]
pret - ty is My La - dy sweet a - rise, a -
[loud]
pret - ty is My La - dy sweet a - rise, a -
[loud]
pret - ty is My La - dy sweet a - rise, a -
35
loud

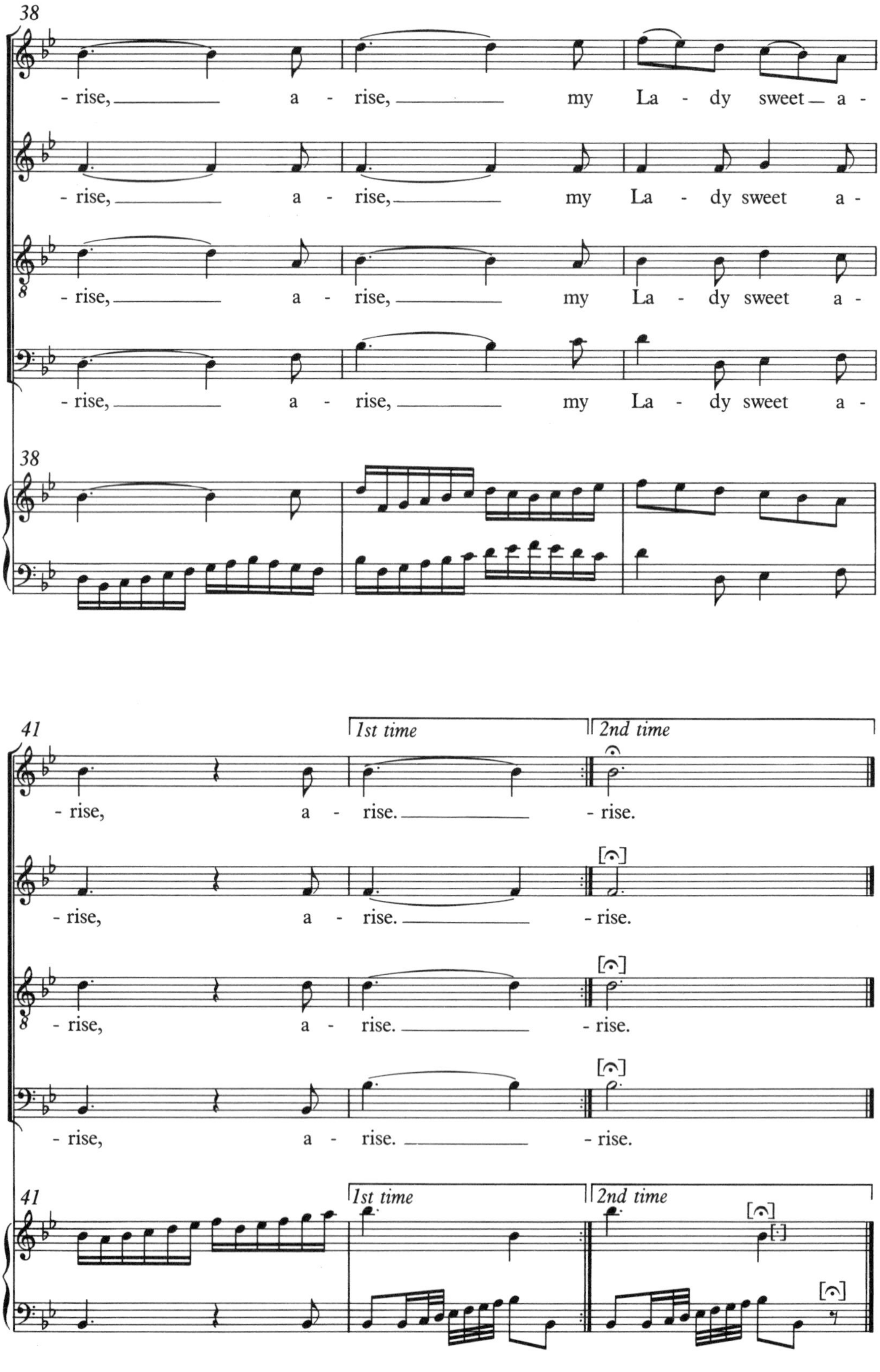

41
1st time
2nd time
- rise, a - rise. - rise.
- rise, a - rise. - rise.
- rise, a - rise. - rise.
- rise, a - rise. - rise.
41
1st time
2nd time

7. Susanna and the two Elders

7
wife-hode well mayn - tayne, Al-gates as-sault - ed so, al-gates as-sault - ed
- hode well mayn-tayne, Al-gates as - sault - ed so,
wife - hode well mayn-tayne, Al-gates as-sault - ed so, al-gates as-sault-ed so, as-
well mayn - tayne, Al-gates as - sault - ed so, al-gates as-
7
10
so, as-sault-ed so by lo - vers twayne, by
al-gates as-sault-ed so by lo - vers twayne, by
- sault - ed so by lo-vers twayne, by lo - vers,
- sault - ed so by lo - vers twayne, by
10

13
1st time
2nd time
lo - vers twayne. lo - vers twayne.
lo - vers twayne. lo - vers twayne. Now as I
lo - vers... twayne. lo - vers... twayne.
lo - vers twayne. lo - vers twayne.
17
Now as I reade a - ryght that aun - cient song, that
reade a - ryght that aun - cient song, as I reade a-ryght that aun-cient song, that
Now as I reade a - ryght that aun - cient song, as I reade a - ryght that
Now as I reade a - ryght that aun -

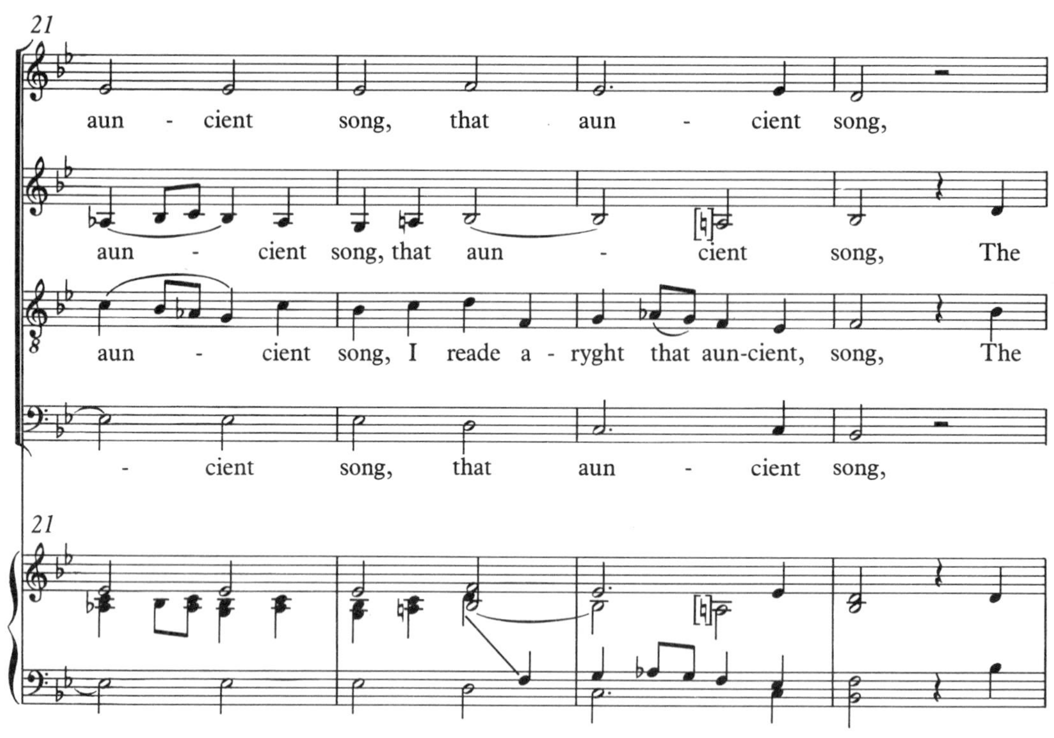
21
aun - cient song, that aun - cient song,
aun - cient song, that aun - cient song, The
aun - cient song, I reade a - ryght that aun-cient, song, The
- cient song, that aun - cient song,
21

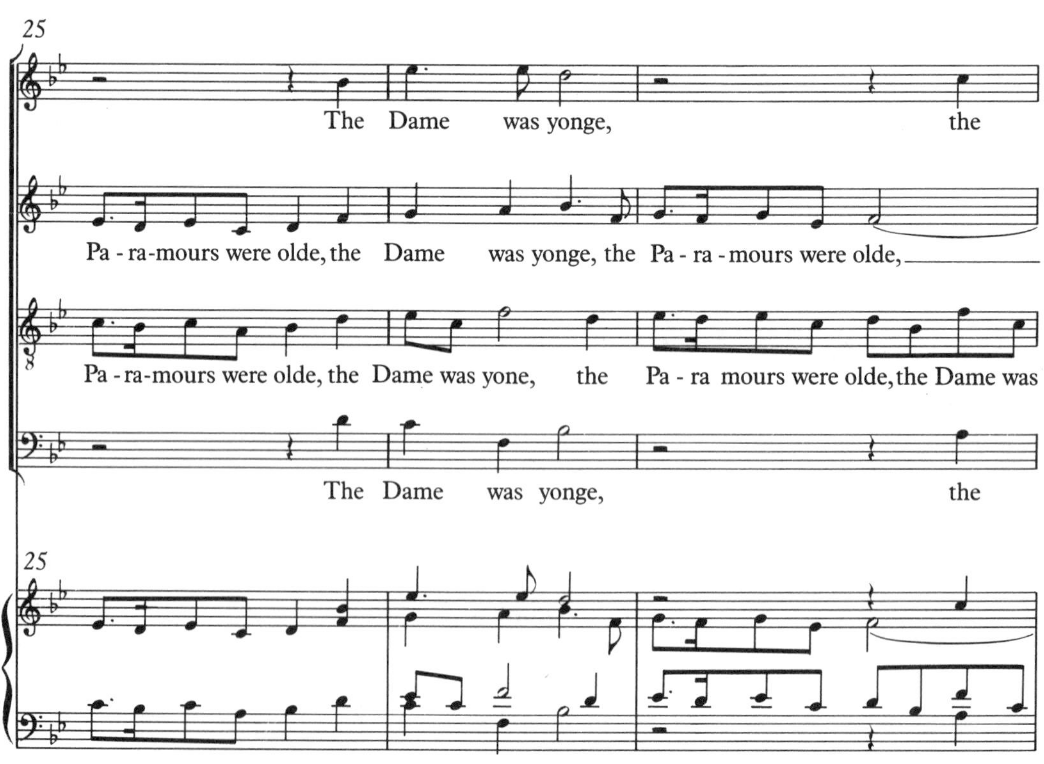
25
The Dame was yonge, the
Pa - ra-mours were olde, the Dame was yonge, the Pa - ra - mours were olde,
Pa - ra-mours were olde, the Dame was yone, the Pa - ra mours were olde, the Dame was
The Dame was yonge, the
25

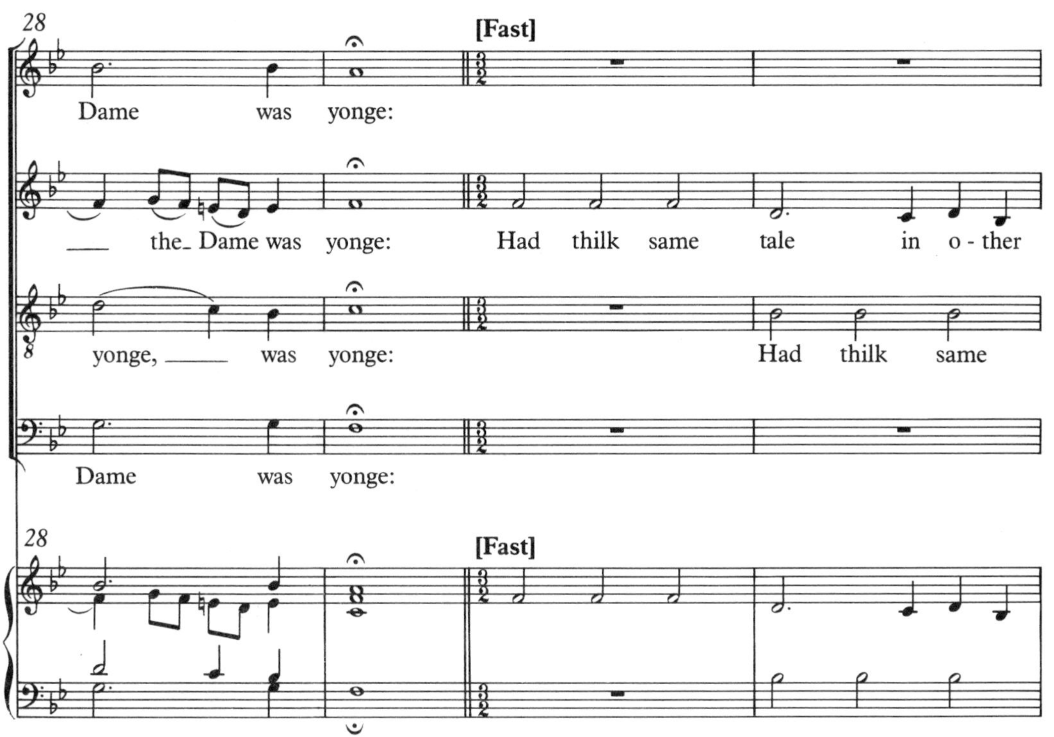
28
[Fast]
Dame was yonge:
the_ Dame was yonge: Had thilk same tale in o - ther
yonge, was yonge: Had thilk same
Dame was yonge:
28
[Fast]

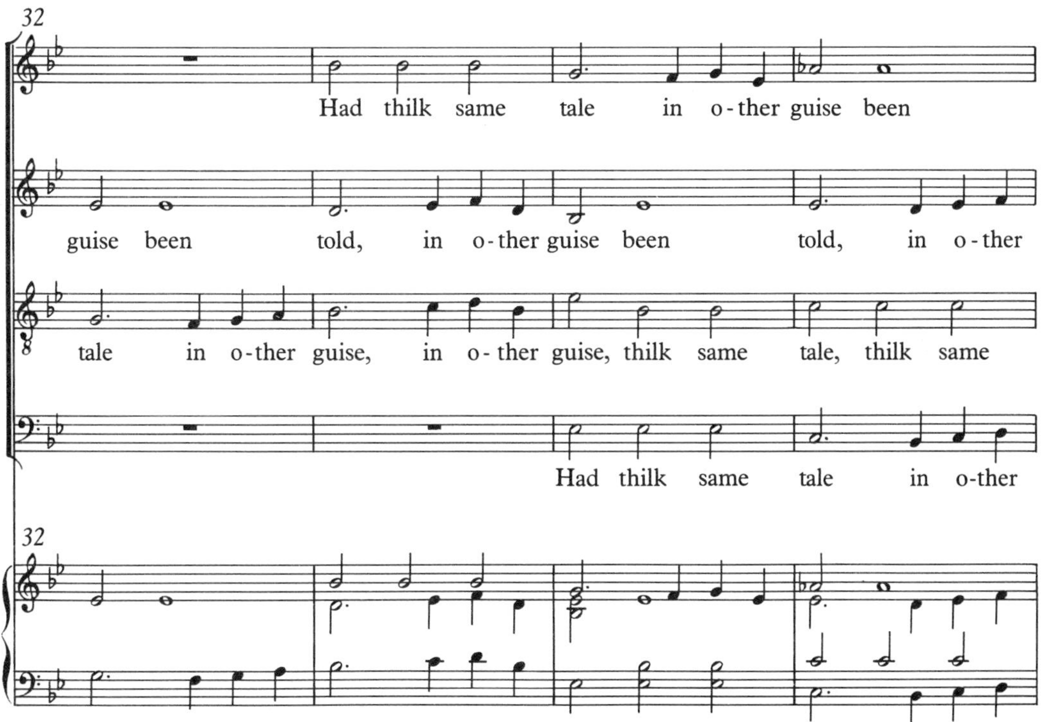
32
Had thilk same tale in o-ther guise been
guise been told, in o-ther guise been told, in o-ther
tale in o-ther guise, in o-ther guise, thilk same tale, thilk same
Had thilk same tale in o-ther
32

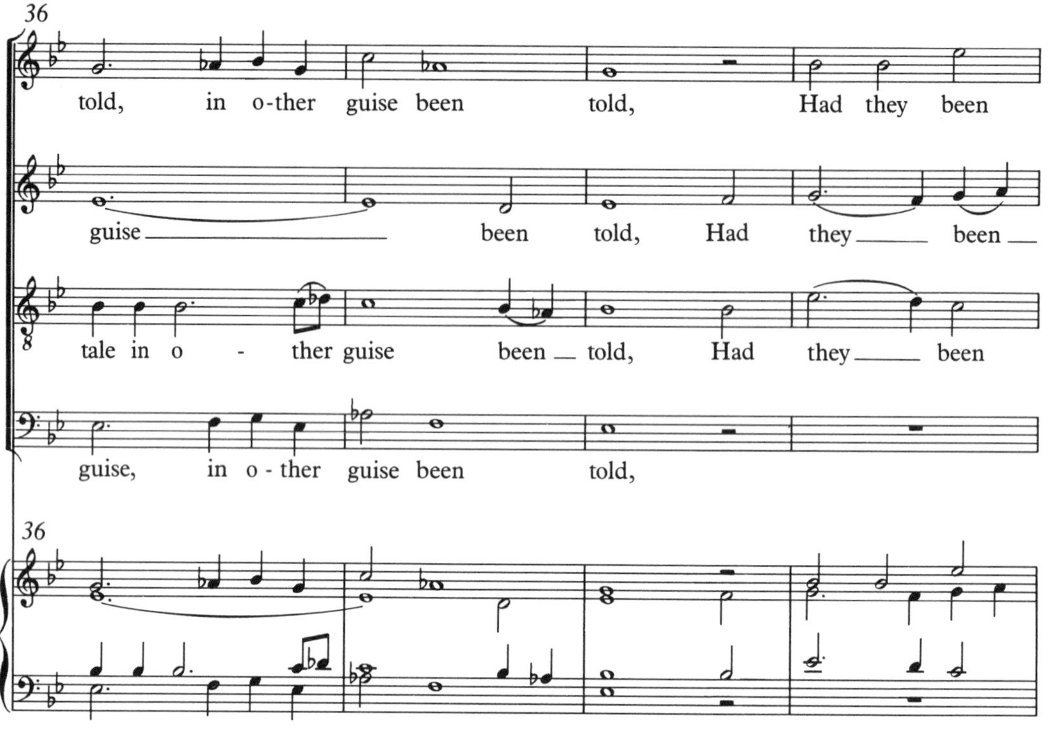
36
told, in o-ther guise been told, Had they been
guise been told, Had they been
tale in o - ther guise been told, Had they been
guise, in o-ther guise been told,
36

40
yonge and she been olde, had they been
yonge and she been olde, had they been
yonge and she been olde, had they
and she been olde, had they been
40

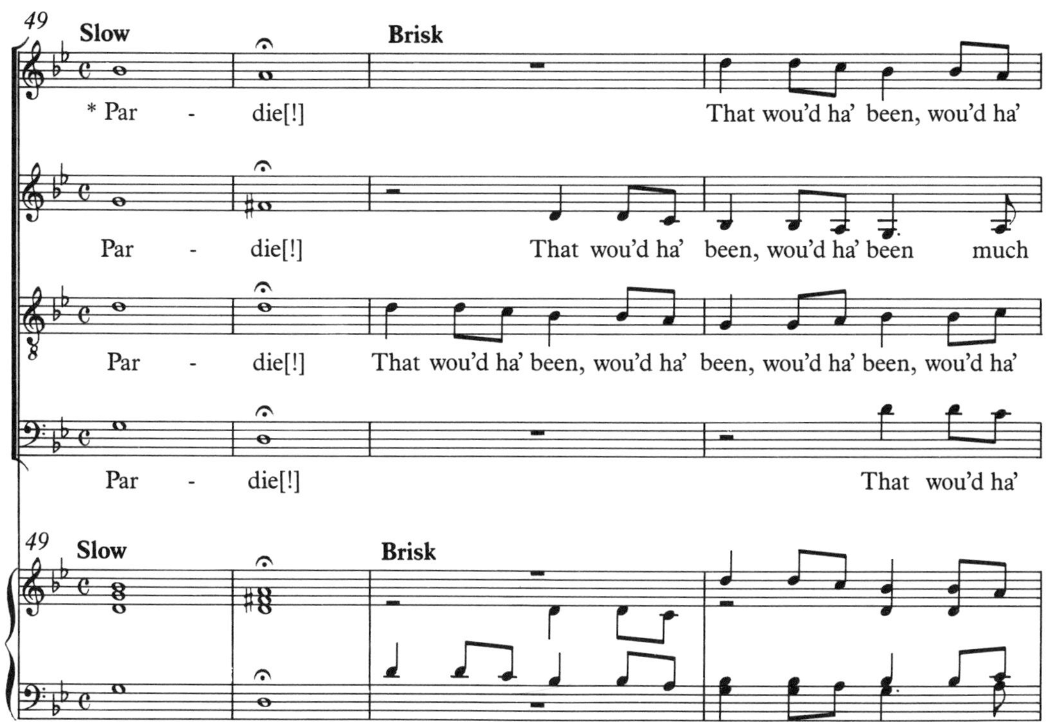

* Pardie = Pardieu (By God)

53
been much so - rer try - ale, Par - die, Par-die[!] That wou'd ha'
so-rer, much so - rer try - ale, much so - rer, much so - rer _ try - -
been much so - rer try - ale, much so - rer try - ale,
been much so - rer try - ale, Par - die, Par - die[!]
53

57
been much so - rer try - ale, that wou'd ha' been much so - rer
- ale, that wou'd ha' been much so - rer try - -
that wou'd ha' been, wou'd ha' been much so - rer try - ale, so - rer
That, that wou'd ha' been, wou'd ha' been much so - rer, so - rer
57

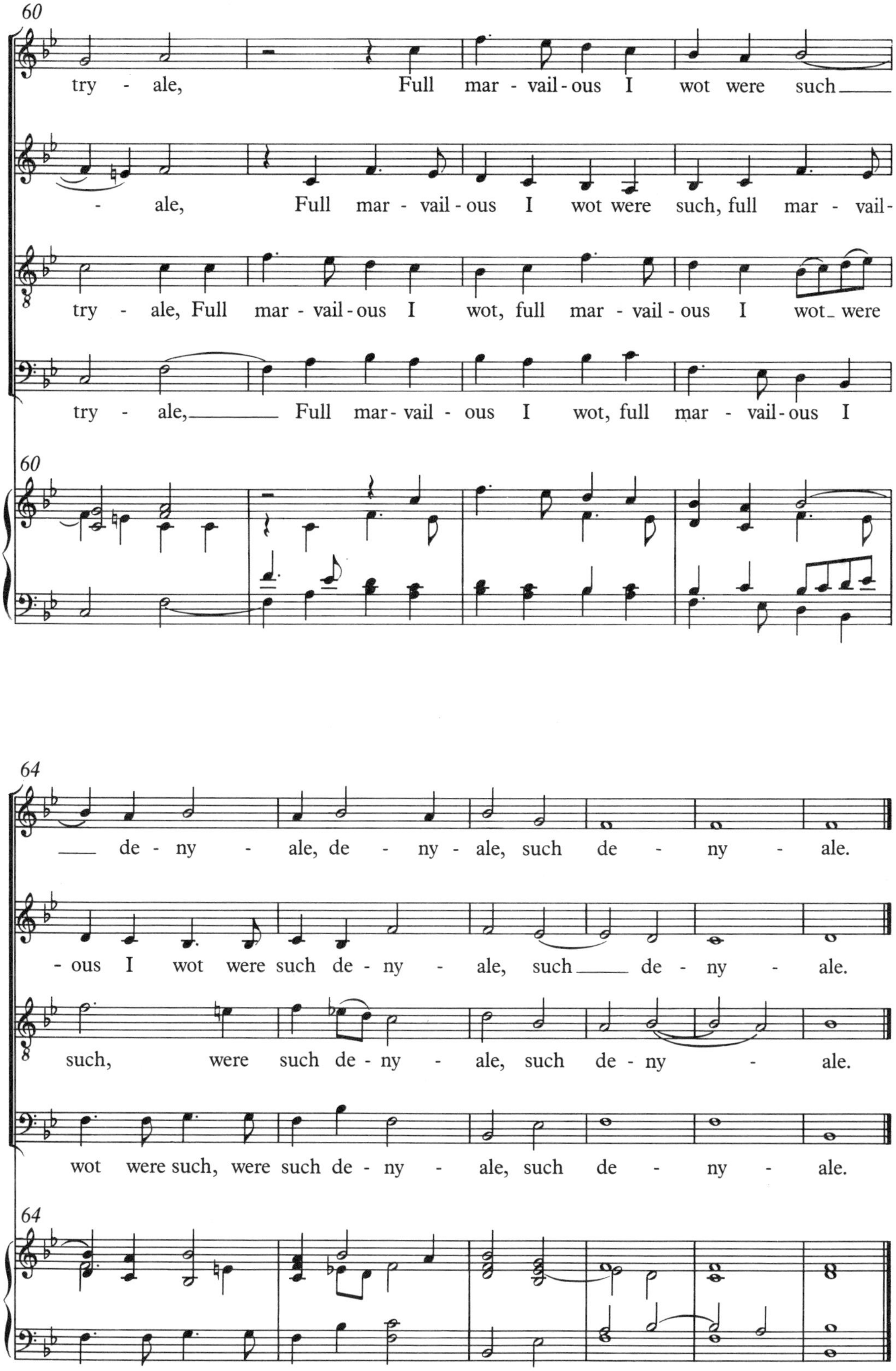

60

try - ale, Full mar - vail - ous I wot were such ___

- ale, Full mar - vail - ous I wot were such, full mar - vail-

try - ale, Full mar - vail - ous I wot, full mar - vail - ous I wot_ were

try - ale,___ Full mar- vail - ous I wot, full mar - vail - ous I

60

8. Long may live my lovely Hetty

SAMUEL JOHNSON
(1709–84)

BENJAMIN COOKE
(1734–93)

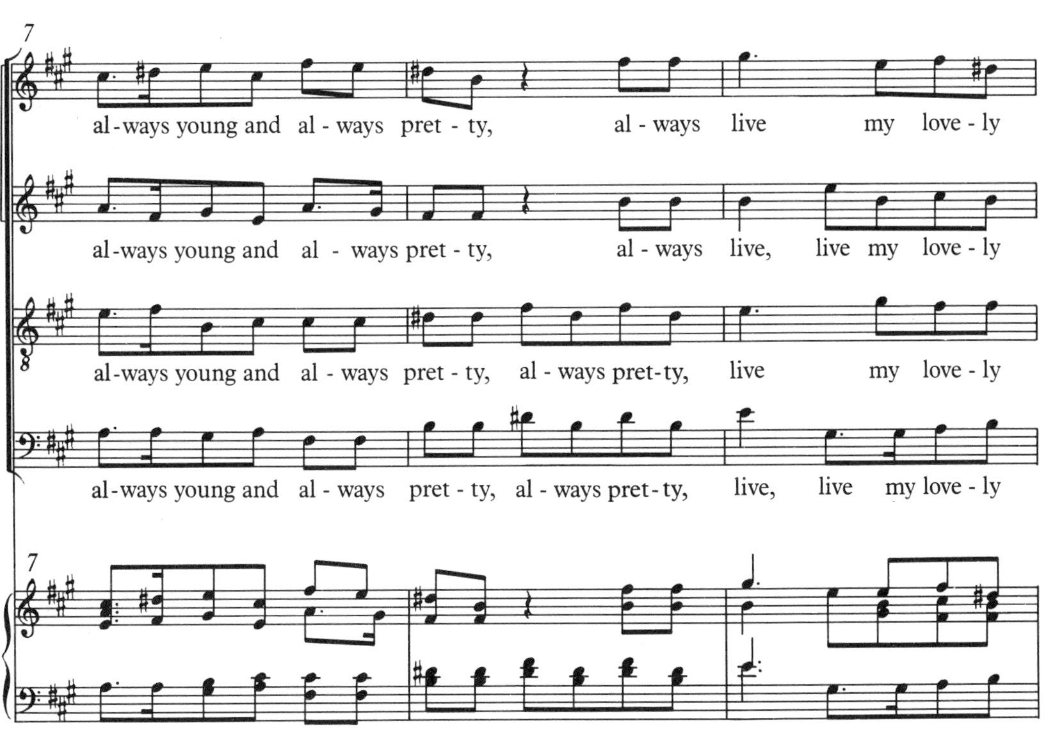
7
al-ways young and al-ways pret-ty, al-ways live my love-ly
al-ways young and al-ways pret-ty, al-ways live, live my love-ly
al-ways young and al-ways pret-ty, al-ways pret-ty, live my love-ly
al-ways young and al-ways pret-ty, al-ways pret-ty, live, live my love-ly
7

10
Het-ty, young and pret-ty; Long may live my love-ly Het-ty, Al-ways young and
Het-ty, live long, Live long,
Het-ty, live long; Long may live my love-ly Het-ty, Al-ways young and
Het-ty, young and pret-ty, Live long,
10

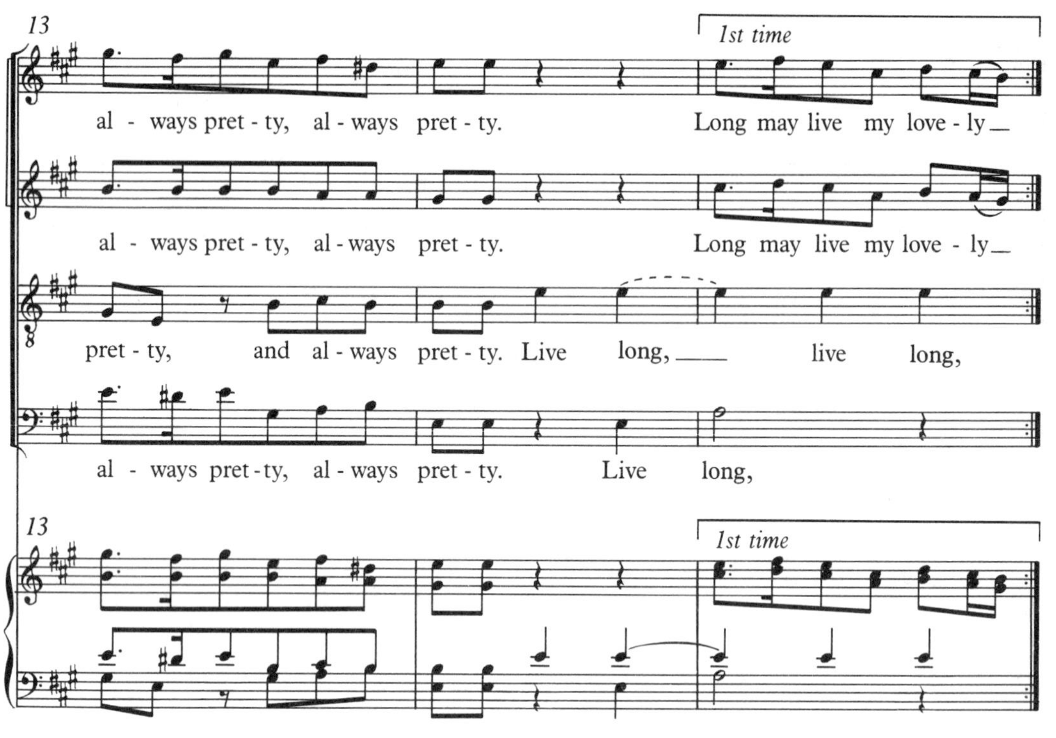
13
1st time
al - ways pret - ty, al - ways pret - ty. Long may live my love - ly
al - ways pret - ty, al - ways pret - ty. Long may live my love - ly
pret - ty, and al - ways pret - ty. Live long, live long,
al - ways pret - ty, al - ways pret - ty. Live long,
13
1st time

16
2nd time
Al - ways pret - ty, al - ways young, Live my love - ly Het - ty
Live long, Al - ways pret - ty, al - ways young, al - ways,
Al - ways pret - ty, al - ways young, Live my love - ly Het - ty
Live long, Al - ways pret - ty, al - ways young,
16
2nd time

19
long, live, live my love - ly Het - ty
al-ways young and al - ways pret - ty, young and pret - ty, live my love - ly Het - ty
long, live long, live, live my love - ly Het - ty,
al-ways young and al - ways pret - ty, live, live my love - ly Het - ty,
19
22
long, live my love - ly Het - ty long,
long, live my love - ly Het - ty long,
Al-ways young and al - ways pret - ty, al-ways young and al - ways
Al-ways young and al - ways pret - ty, al-ways young and al - ways
22

25
Adagio
al - ways pret - ty, al - ways young, al - ways
al - ways pret - ty, al - ways young, al - ways
pret - ty, al - ways pret - ty, al - ways young, al - ways
pret - ty, al - ways pret - ty, al - ways young, al - ways
25
Adagio

29
1st time
2nd time
A little quicker
[SOLO]
pret - ty. pret - ty. Long may live my love - ly
pret - ty. pret - ty.
[SOLO]
pret - ty. Live long, pret - ty. Long may live my love - ly
[SOLO]
pret - ty. Live, pret - ty. Long live my love - ly
29
1st time
2nd time
A little quicker

33
CHORUS
Het - ty, Al - ways young and al - ways pret - ty, Al - ways pret - ty, al - ways
[CHORUS]
Al - ways young and al - ways pret - ty, Al - ways pret - ty, al - ways
[CHORUS]
Het - ty, Al - ways young and al - ways pret - ty, Al - ways pret - ty, al - ways
CHORUS
Het - ty, Al - ways pret - ty, al - ways
33
37
SOLO
young, Live my love - ly Het - ty long, Al-ways young and al - ways pret - ty, Long may
young, Live my love - ly Het - ty long, Al-ways young and al - ways pret - ty,
young, Live my love - ly Het - ty long, Al-ways young and al - ways pret - ty,
SOLO
young, Live my love - ly Het - ty long, Al-ways young and al - ways pret - ty, Long may
37

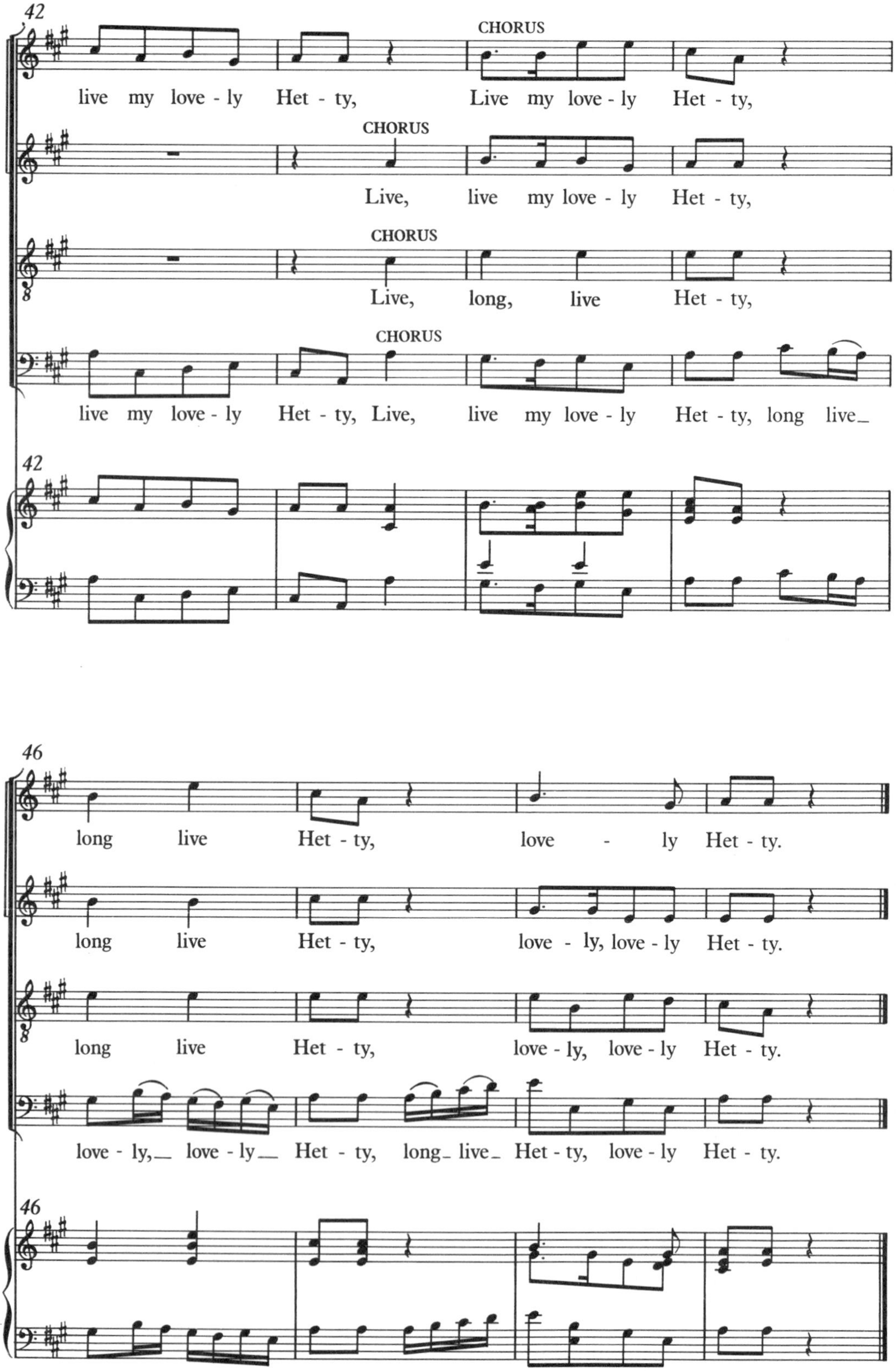

42

CHORUS

live my love - ly Het - ty, Live my love - ly Het - ty,

CHORUS

Live, live my love - ly Het - ty,

CHORUS

Live, long, live Het - ty,

CHORUS

live my love - ly Het - ty, Live, live my love - ly Het - ty, long live_

42

9. Lady Anne Bothwell's Lament

SCOTTISH FOLK-SONG
from Thomas Percy (1729–1801)
Reliques of Ancient English Poetry

JOSEPH CORFE
(1740–1820)

5
- low my babe, lye still and sleep, It
weep, Ba - low my babe, lye still and sleep,
weep, Ba - low my babe, lye still and sleep, It
weep, Ba - low my babe, lye still and sleep,
5
7
grieves me sair to see thee weep, If
to see thee weep,
grieves me sair to see thee weep,
to see thee weep, If
7

9
thou'lt be si - lent I'll be glad,
If thou'lt be si - lent I'll be glad, Thy
If thou'lt be si - lent I'll be glad, Thy
thou'lt be si - lent I'll be glad,
9
11
Ba -
main - ing makes my heart full sad.
main - ing makes my heart full sad.
11

13

-low, my babe, thy mi - ther's joy, Thy

Ba - low, my babe, thy mi - ther's joy, Thy

Ba - low, my babe, thy mi - ther's joy, Thy

Ba - low, my babe, thy mi - ther's joy, Thy

13

15

[*Fine*]

fa - ther breeds thee great an - noy. If

fa - ther breeds thee great an - noy.

fa - ther breeds thee great an - noy.

fa - ther breeds thee great an - noy. If

15

[*Fine*]

10. Ring out ye crystal spheres

JOHN MILTON
(1608–74)

WILLIAM CROTCH
(1775–1847)

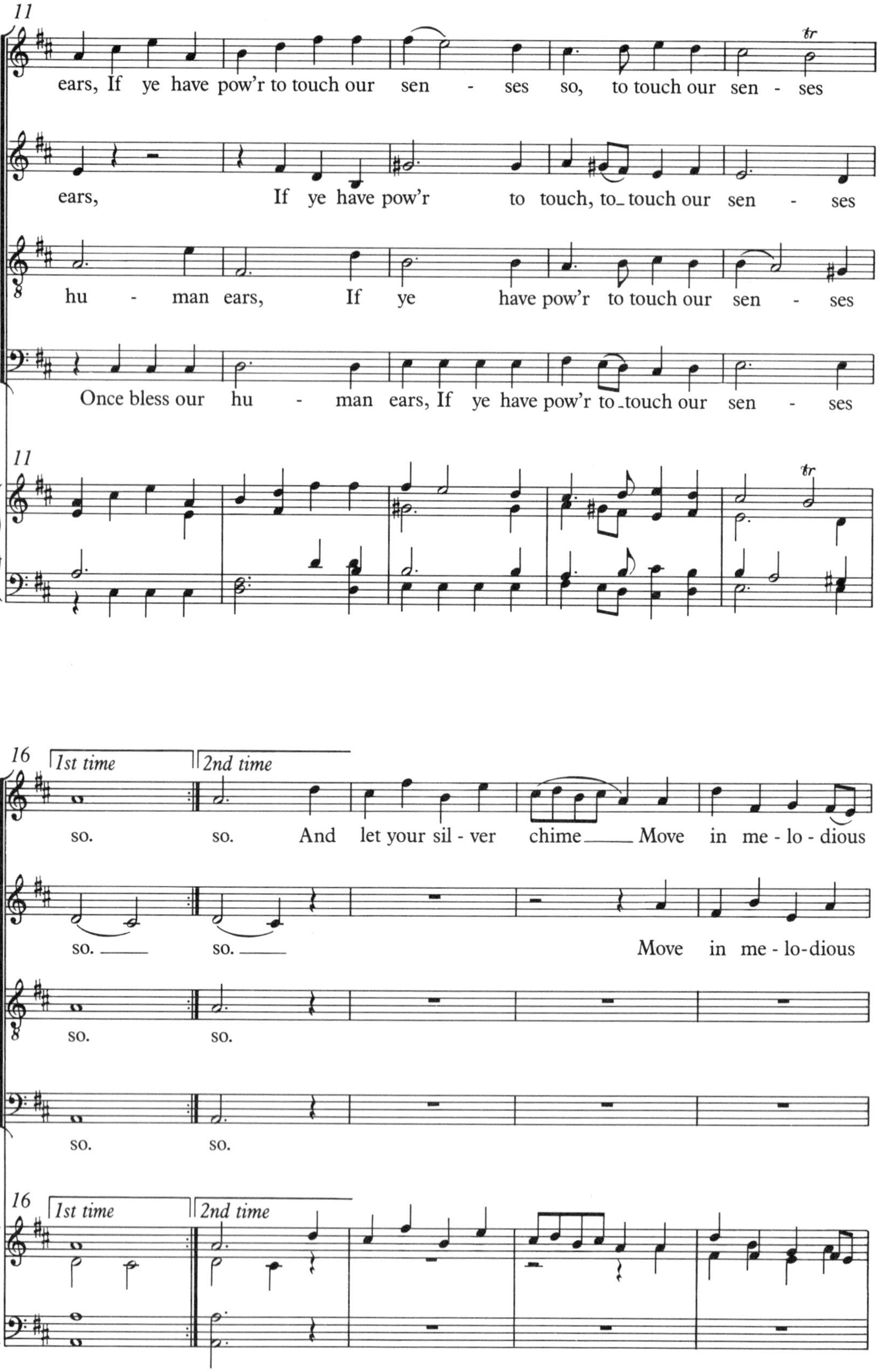

11

ears, If ye have pow'r to touch our sen - ses so, to touch our sen - ses

ears, If ye have pow'r to touch, to touch our sen - ses

hu - man ears, If ye have pow'r to touch our sen - ses

Once bless our hu - man ears, If ye have pow'r to touch our sen - ses

11

21
time, move in me - lo - dious time,
time,
And let the bass of
And let your sil - ver chime, And let the bass of
And let your sil - ver chime, And let the bass of
21
26
And let your sil - ver chime Move
heav'ns deep or - gan blow,
heav'ns deep or - gan blow, And
heav'ns deep or - gan blow,
26

31
in me - lo-dious time,
And with your
your sil - ver chime,
And with your nine - fold
let your sil - ver chime,
And with your nine - fold har - mo -
And let the bass of heav'ns deep or - gan blow,
31

36
nine - fold har - mo - ny
Make up full con - cert
har - mo - ny
Make up full con - cert, make up full
- ny, your nine-fold har - mo - ny, your har - mo - ny Make up full con - cert
And with your nine-fold har - mo - ny, your
36

41
to th'an - ge - lic sym - pho - ny,
con - cert to th'an - ge - lic sym - pho - ny, And let the bass of
to th'an - ge - lic sym-pho - ny, And let the bass of
nine - fold har - mo - ny, And let the bass of
41
46
And let your sil - ver chime Move
heav'ns deep or - gan blow, Move
heav'ns deep or - gan blow,
heav'ns deep or - gan blow,
46

51
in me - lo - dious time, And with your nine - fold har - mo -
in me - lo - dious time, And with your nine - fold har - mo -
And with your nine - fold, nine - fold har - mo -
51
56
- ny Make up full con - cert to th'an - ge - lic sym - pho - ny.
- ny Make up full con - cert to th'an - ge - lic sym - pho - ny.
- ny Make up full con - cert to th'an - ge - lic sym - pho - ny.
Make up full con - cert to th'an - ge - lic sym - pho - ny.
56

11. The Nightingale

ANON. | JOHN DANBY (1757–98)

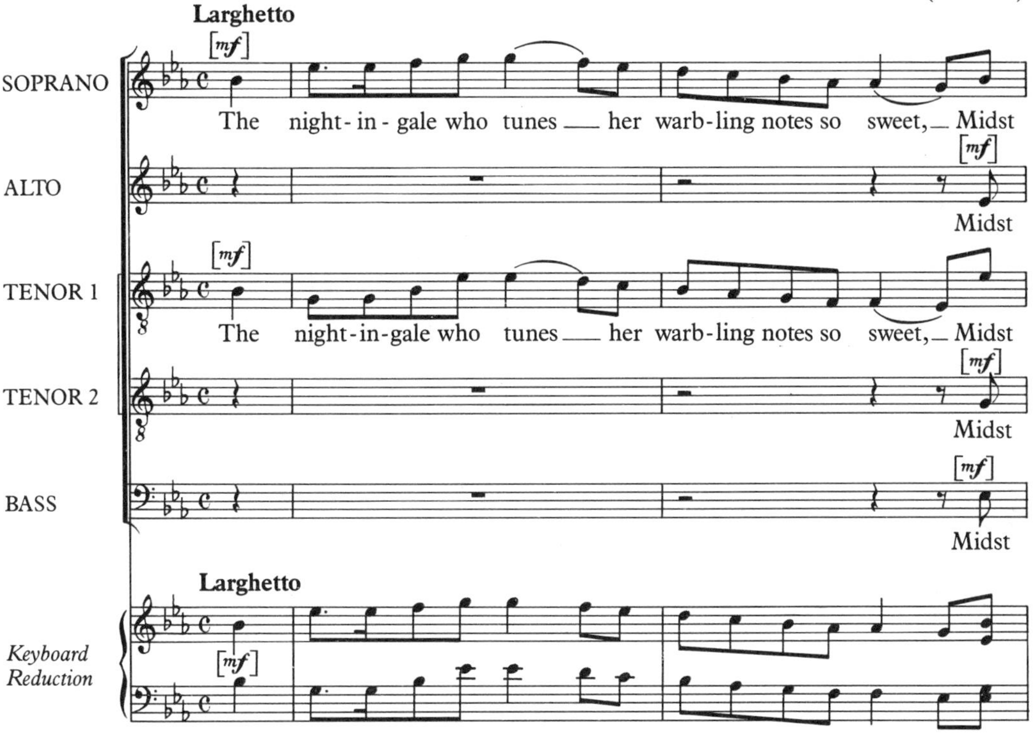

Larghetto
[mf]
SOPRANO
The night-in-gale who tunes her warb-ling notes so sweet, Midst
ALTO
[mf]
Midst
TENOR 1
[mf]
The night-in-gale who tunes her warb-ling notes so sweet, Midst
TENOR 2
[mf]
Midst
BASS
[mf]
Midst
Larghetto
Keyboard Reduction
[mf]

3
flow-ers ne'er pre-sumes to fix her mourn-ful seat,
flow-ers ne'er pre-sumes to fix her mourn-ful seat,
flow-ers ne'er pre-sumes to fix her mourn-ful seat, The
flow-ers ne'er pre-sumes to fix her mourn-ful seat,
flow-ers ne'er pre-sumes to fix her mourn-ful seat,
3

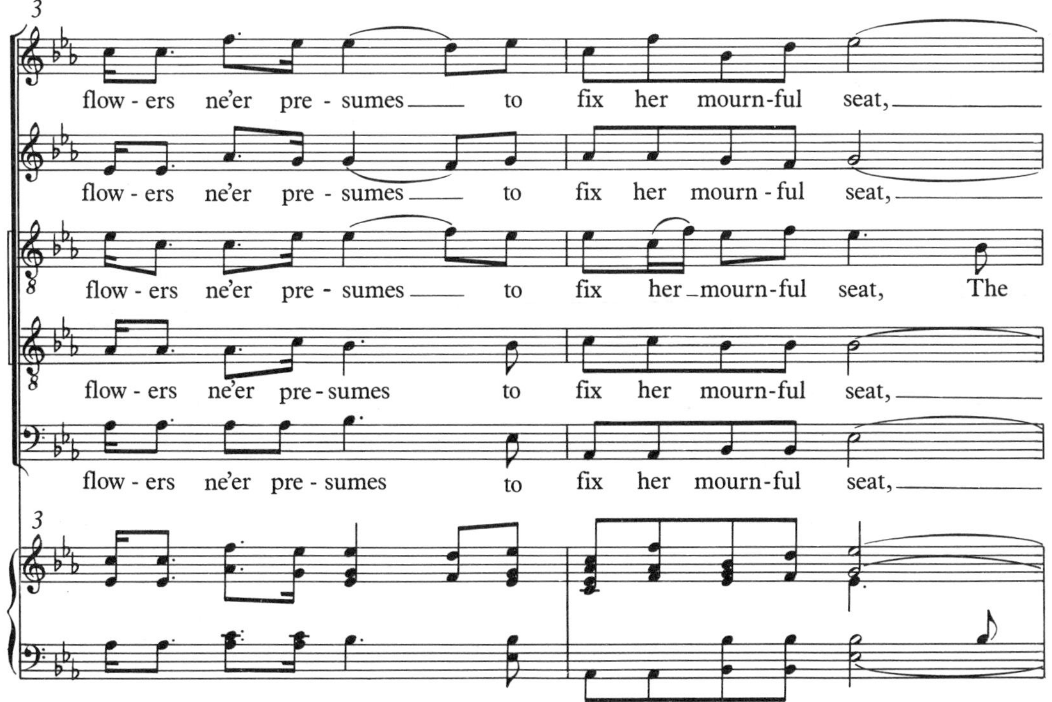

5

The

her warb-ling notes so sweet,

night-in-gale who tunes her warb-ling notes so sweet,

The night-in-gale who tunes her warb-ling notes so

5

7

night - in-gale who tunes her warb - ling notes so

her warb-ling notes so

her warb-ling notes so

sweet, the night - in-gale who tunes her warb-ling notes so

The night - in-gale who tunes her warb-ling notes so

7

9

p

sweet, to

p

sweet, 'Midst flow - ers ne'er pre - sumes to fix her mourn-ful

p

sweet, 'Midst flow - ers ne'er pre - sumes to fix her mourn-ful

p

sweet, 'Midst flow - ers ne'er pre - sumes to

p

sweet, 'Midst flow - ers ne'er pre - sumes to

9

p

11

f *dim.*

fix her mourn-ful seat, to fix her mourn - ful,

f *dim.*

seat, 'midst flow - ers ne'er pre-sumes to fix her

f *dim.*

seat, 'midst flow - ers ne'er pre - sumes to fix her

f *dim.*

fix her mourn-ful seat, 'midst flow - ers ne'er pre -

[*f*] [*dim.*]

fix her mourn-ful seat, 'midst flow - ers ne'er pre -

11

f *dim.*

13
p
f
mourn-ful seat, to fix her mourn - ful seat,
mourn - ful seat, to fix her mourn - ful seat,
mourn - ful seat, to fix her mourn - ful, mourn - ful seat,
- sumes, ne'er pre-sumes to fix her mourn - ful seat,
- sumes to fix her mourn - ful seat,
13
[mf]
16
Me - lo - dious - ly she sings,
Me - lo - - dious - ly she
Me - lo - dious - ly she sings, me - lo - dious - ly she
Me - lo - dious - ly she
16

18
me - lo - dious - ly she sings, she sings me -
sings, me - lo - dious - ly she sings,
sings, me - lo - dious - ly she sings,
sings, she sings me - lo - dious - ly,
[mf]
Me - lo - dious - ly she sings, me - lo - dious - ly she
18
20
ff
- lo - dious-ly, while haw - thorns pierce her
ff
while haw - thorns pierce her
ff
while haw-thorns pierce her breast, while haw-thorns pierce her
ff
she sings me - lo - dious - ly, while haw - thorns pierce her
ff
sings, while haw - thorns pierce her
20
ff

22
p
breast, Her voice sweet e - cho rings, e - cho rings,
breast, Her voice sweet e - cho rings, e - cho rings,
breast, Her voice sweet e - cho rings,
breast, Her voice sweet e - cho rings,
breast, Her voice sweet e - - - - cho
22
p
25
f
her voice sweet e- cho, her voice sweet e-cho rings,
her voice sweet e-cho, her voice sweet e-cho
e-cho rings, her voice sweet e-cho, her voice sweet e-cho rings, and na -
e-cho rings, her voice sweet e-cho, her voice sweet e-cho rings,
rings, her voice sweet e-cho rings, and
25
f

28
dim.
tr
p
and na-ture lulls to rest, and na-ture
rings, and na-ture lulls to rest, and na-ture
- ture lulls to rest, lulls to rest, and na-ture
and na-ture lulls to rest, lulls to rest, and na-ture
na - ture lulls to rest, lulls to rest, and na-ture
31
[dim.]
pp
lulls to rest.
lulls to rest, lulls to rest.
lulls to rest, and na - ture lulls to rest.
lulls to rest, and na - ture lulls to rest.
lulls to rest.

12. Take, O take those lips away

SHAKESPEARE
(1564–1616)
(*Measure for Measure*, IV. i)

JAMES ELLIOTT
(1783–1856)

8
- sworn; And those eyes, the break of
- sworn; And those eyes, the
- sworn;
- sworn;
8
12
day, those eyes, the break of day,
break of day, the break of day,
And those eyes, the break of day,
12

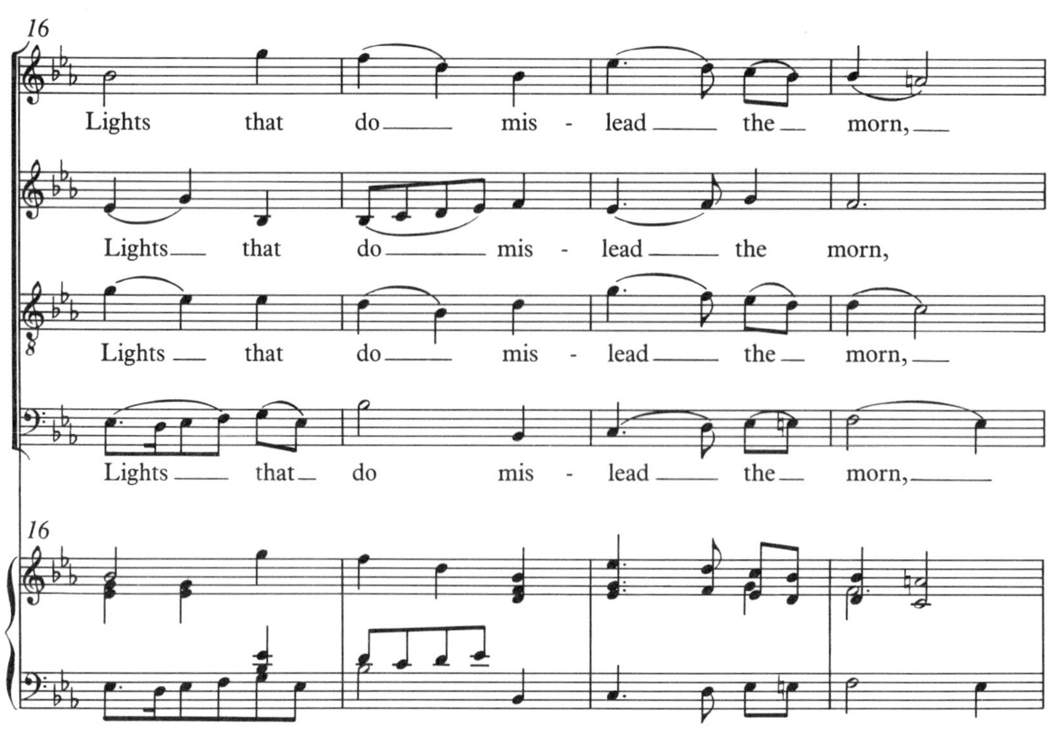

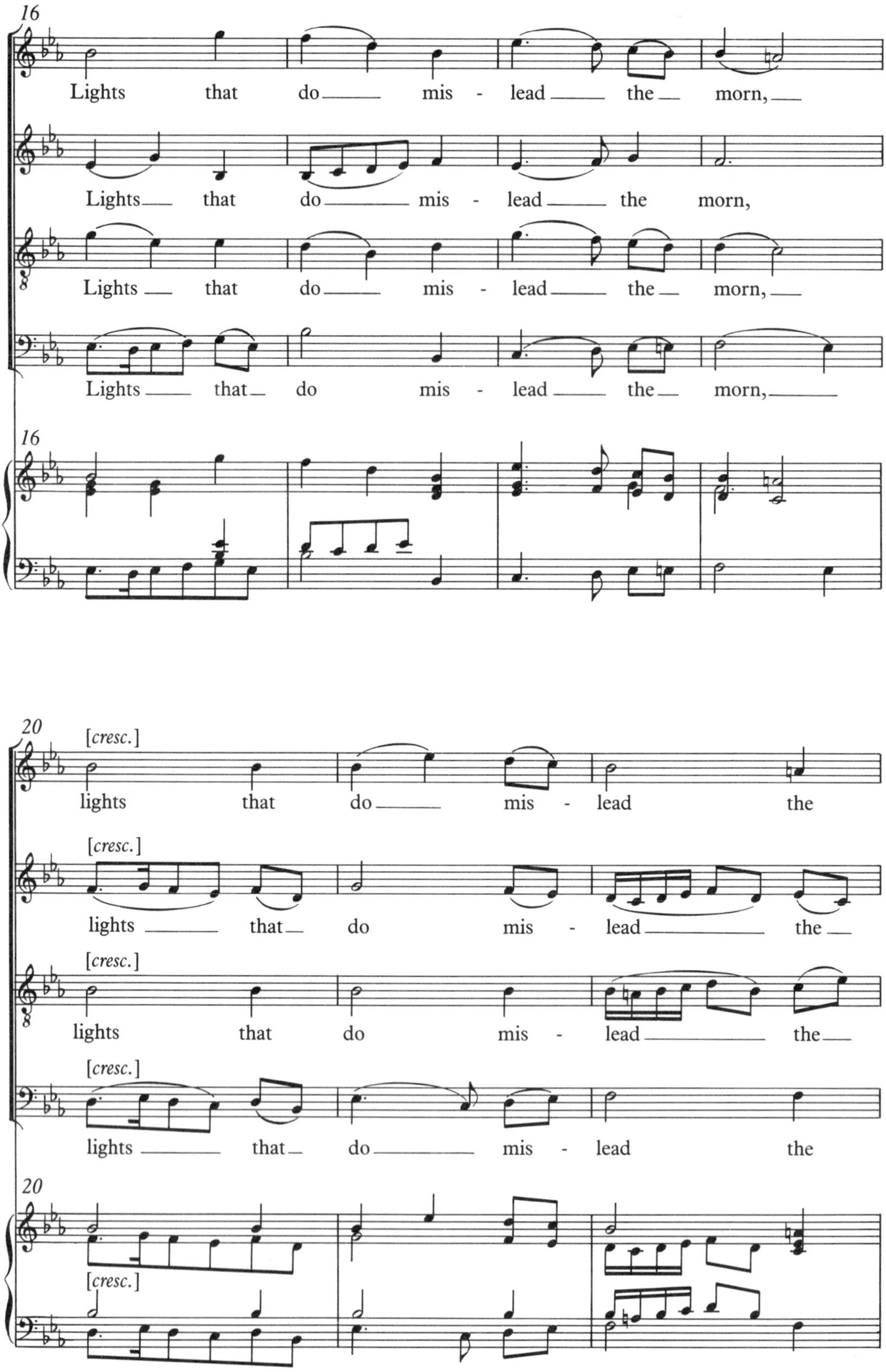

20
[cresc.]
lights that do mis - lead the
[cresc.]
lights that do mis - lead the
[cresc.]
lights that do mis - lead the
[cresc.]
lights that do mis - lead the
20
[cresc.]

23
[f]
morn, mis-lead the morn, mis-lead the morn, that do mis-
[f]
morn, mis-lead the morn, mis-lead the morn, that do mis-
[f]
morn, mis-lead the morn, mis-lead the morn, that do mis-
[f]
morn, that do mis-
23
[f]
26
tr
[3]
-lead the morn.
[3]
[tr]
[mf]
-lead the morn. But my kiss-es
[tr]
[mf]
[3]
-lead the morn. But my kiss-es
[mf]
-lead the morn. But my
26
tr
3
3
[mf]

29
[mf]
But my kiss-es bring a - gain,
bring a - gain, a - gain, my kiss-es bring a -
bring a - gain, my kiss-es bring a -
kiss - es bring a - gain, a - gain;
29

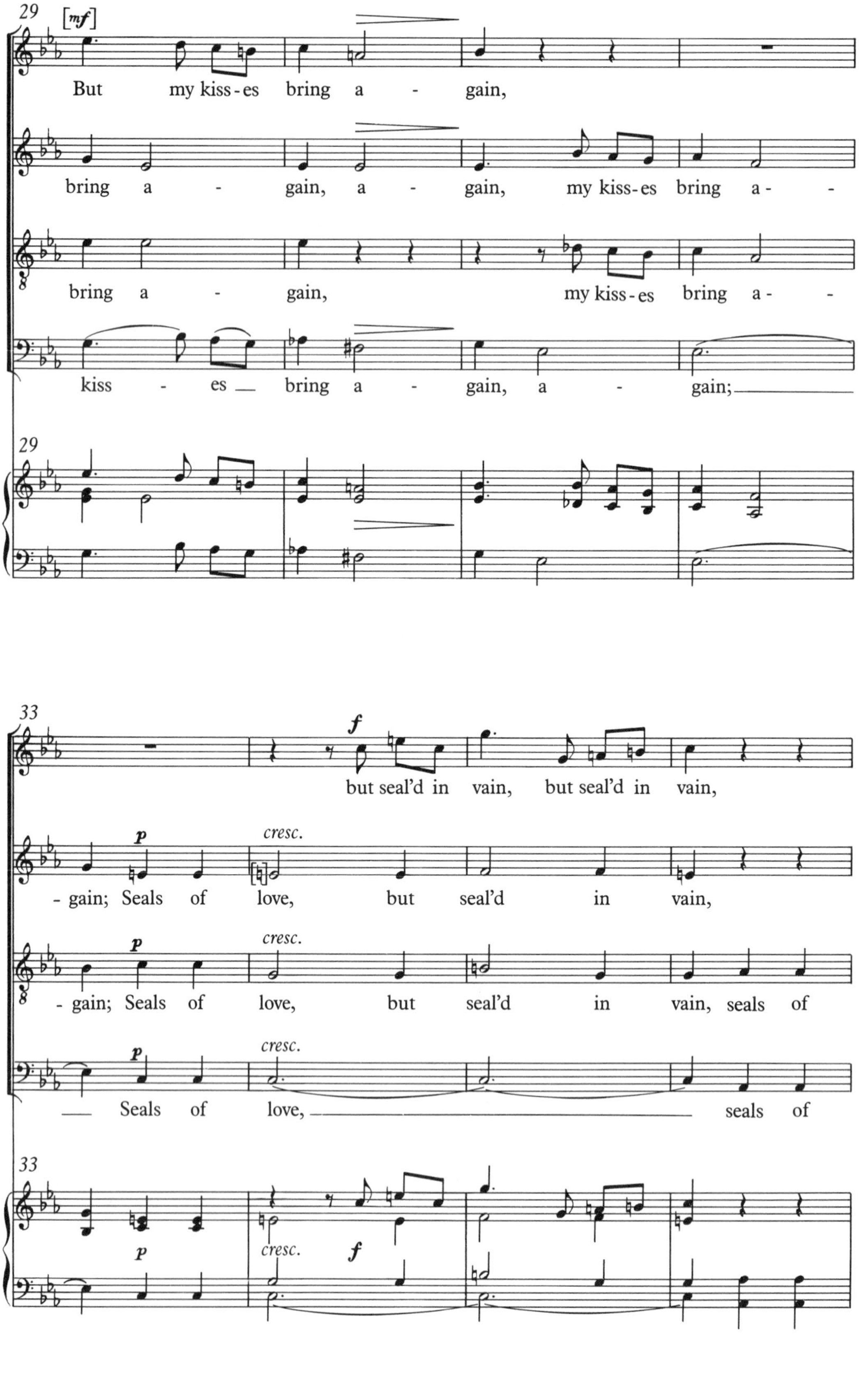

33
f
but seal'd in vain, but seal'd in vain,
p cresc.
- gain; Seals of love, but seal'd in vain,
p cresc.
- gain; Seals of love, but seal'd in vain, seals of
p cresc.
Seals of love, seals of
33
p cresc. f

37
but seal'd in vain, but seal'd in vain, seals of
but seal'd in vain, seals of love, seals of
love, but seal'd in vain, in vain, seals of
love, but seal'd in vain, in vain, seals of
37
41
love, but seal'd in vain,
love, but seal'd in vain,
love, but seal'd in vain, but seal'd in
love, but seal'd in vain, but seal'd in
41

44
but seal'd in vain, but seal'd in vain, seals of
vain, but seal'd in vain, seals of
vain, but seal'd in vain, seals of
44

47
love, of love, but seal'd in vain.
seals of love, but seal'd in vain.
love, love, but seal'd in vain.
love, but seal'd in vain.
47

13. Slow, slow, fresh fount

BEN JONSON
(*c.*1573–1637)
(*Cynthia's Revels*, I. ii)

WILLIAM HORSLEY
(1774–1858)

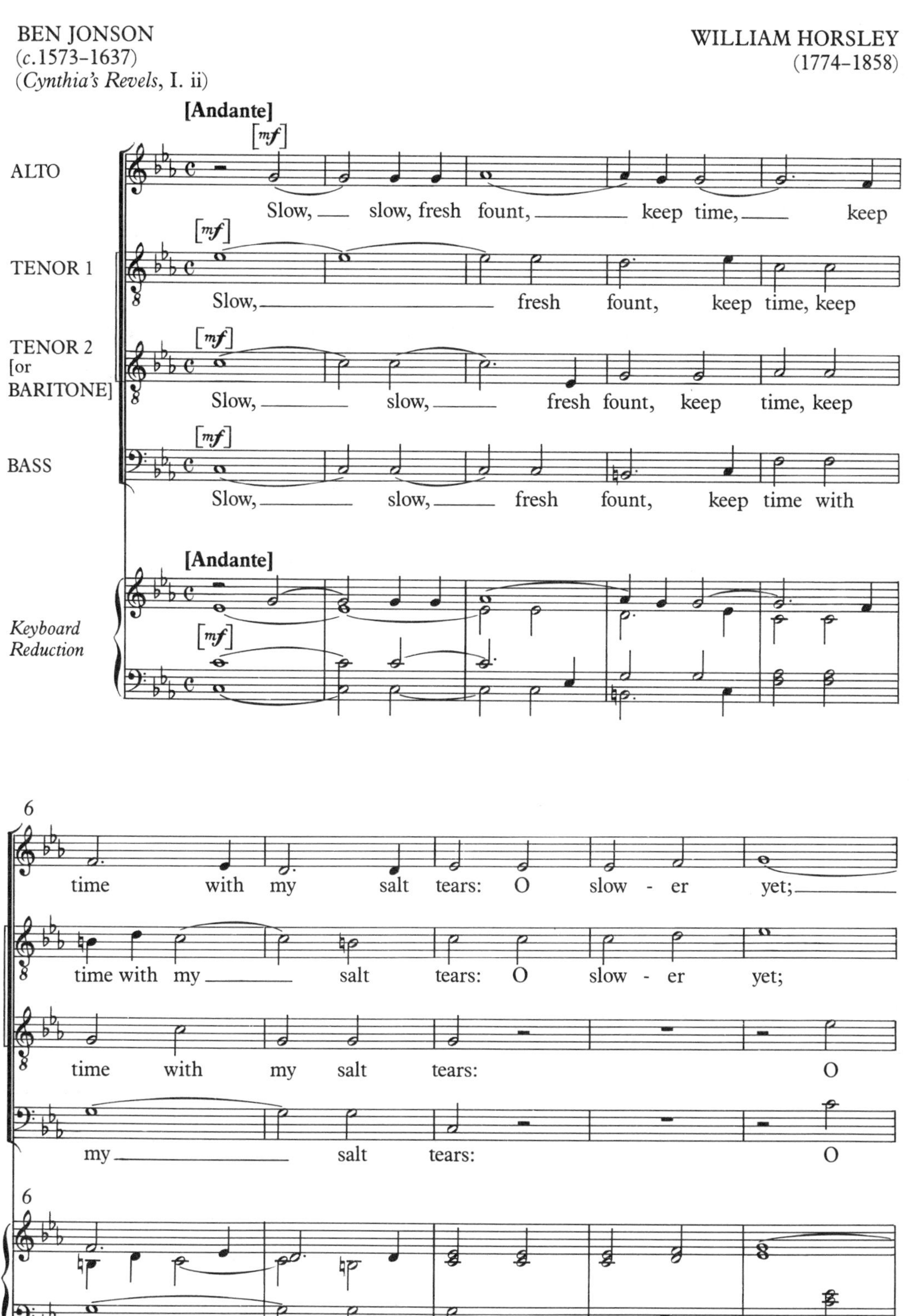

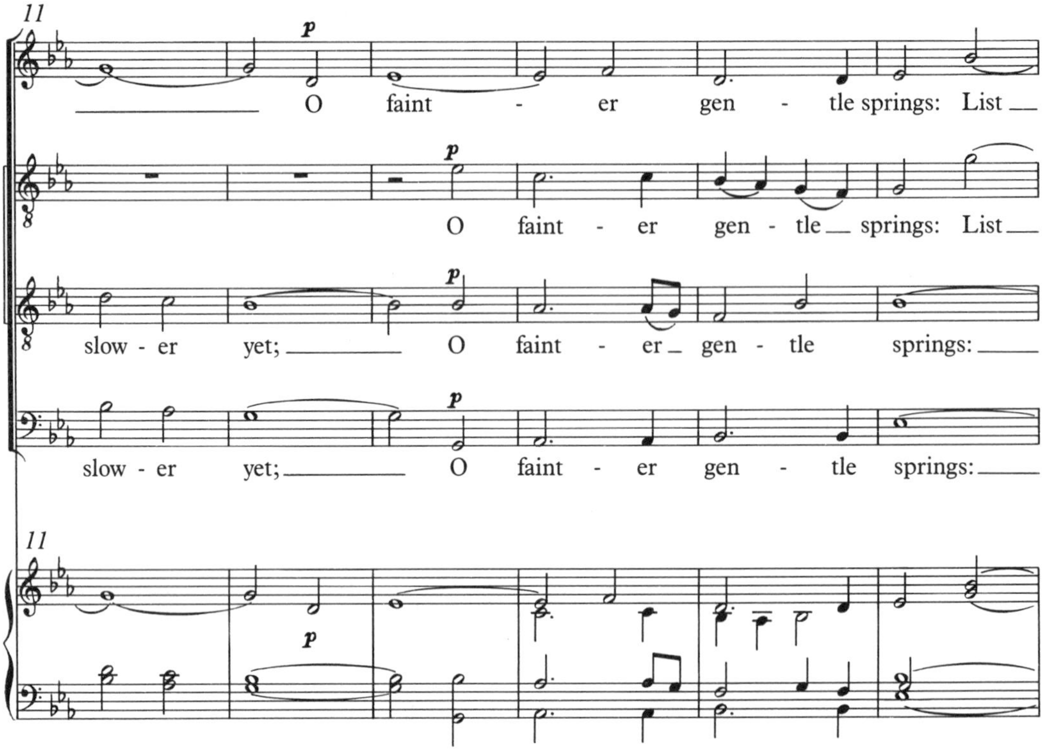

11
p
O faint - er gen - tle springs: List
O faint - er gen - tle springs: List
slow - er yet; O faint - er gen - tle springs:
slow - er yet; O faint - er gen - tle springs:
11
p

17
to the hea - vy part, list to the hea - vy part the
to the hea - vy part, list to the hea - vy part the
List to the hea - vy part, list to the hea - vy part the
List to the hea - vy part, list to the hea - vy part the
17

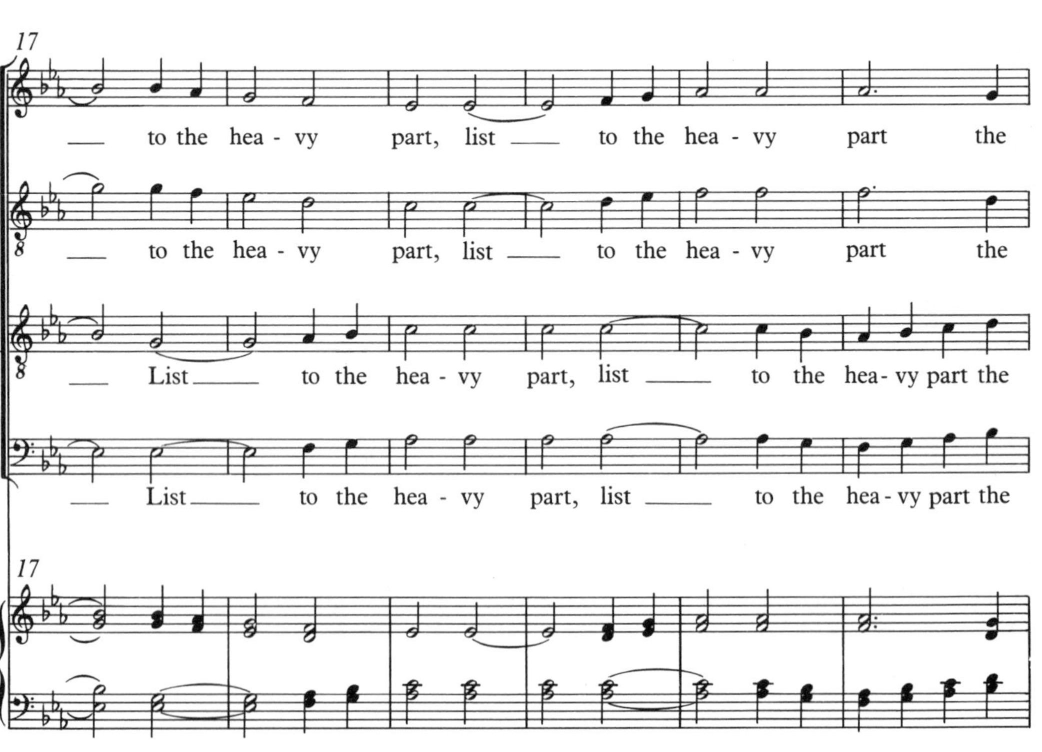

23
pp
mu - sic bears, Woe weeps out, woe weeps
mu - sic bears, Woe weeps out, woe
mu - sic bears, Woe weeps, woe weeps
mu - sic bears, Woe weeps out, woe weeps
23
pp

28
out, weeps out her di - vi - sion when she sings.
weeps out her di - vi - sion when she sings.
out her di - vi - sion when she sings.
out her di - vi - sion when she sings.
28

33
cresc.
Droop, herbs and flow'rs, Fall grief in show'rs, Our beau -
Droop, herbs and flow'rs, Fall grief in show'rs, Our beau -
Droop, herbs and flow'rs, Fall grief in show'rs, Our beau -
Droop, herbs and flow'rs, Fall grief in show'rs, Our beau -
33

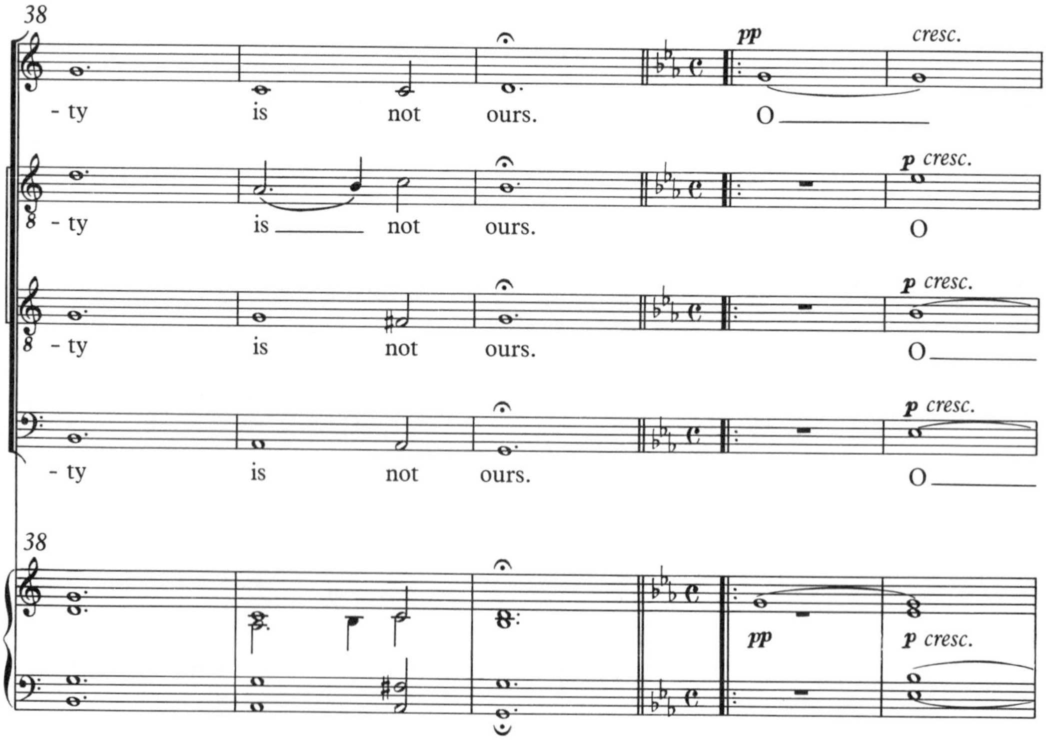
38
pp
cresc.
p cresc.
- ty is not ours. O
- ty is not ours. O
- ty is not ours. O
- ty is not ours. O
38

43
could I still like melt - ing snow up - on some
could I still like melt - ing snow up -
could I still like melt - ing snow up - on some
could I still like melt - ing snow up -
43

47
pp
crag - gy hill fall down, fall
- on some crag - gy hill fall down, fall
p
crag - gy hill fall down, fall
- on some crag - gy hill fall down, fall
47
p
pp

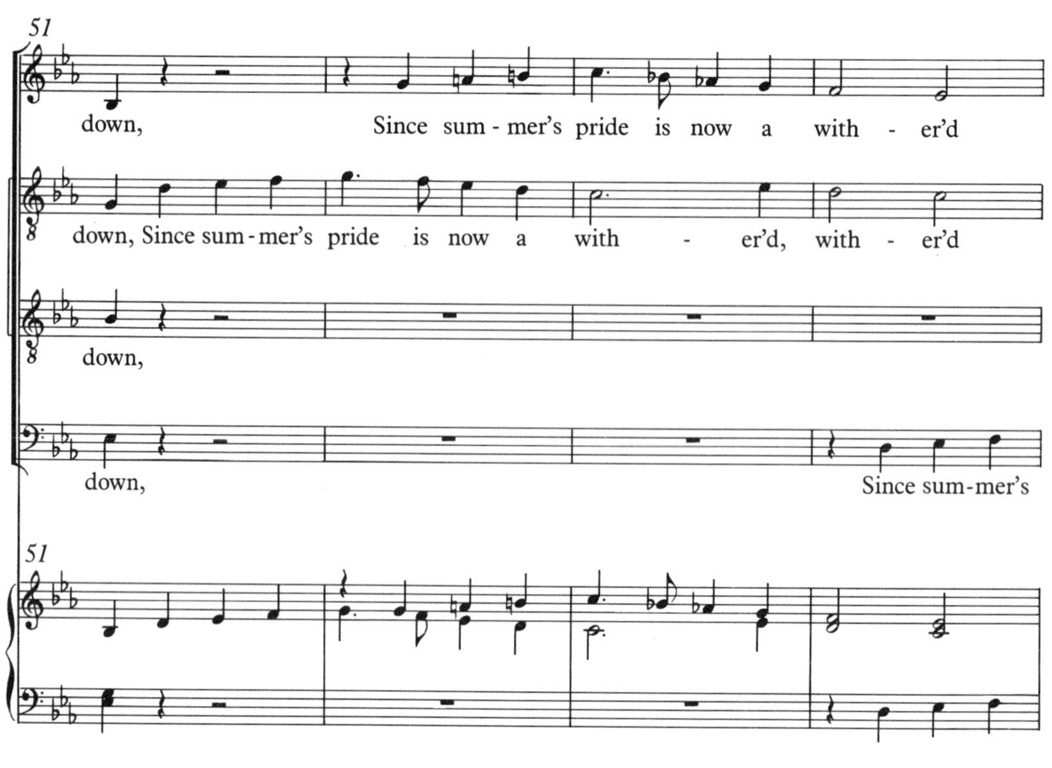
51
down,
Since sum-mer's pride is now a with - er'd
down, Since sum-mer's pride is now a with - er'd, with - er'd
down,
down,
Since sum-mer's
51

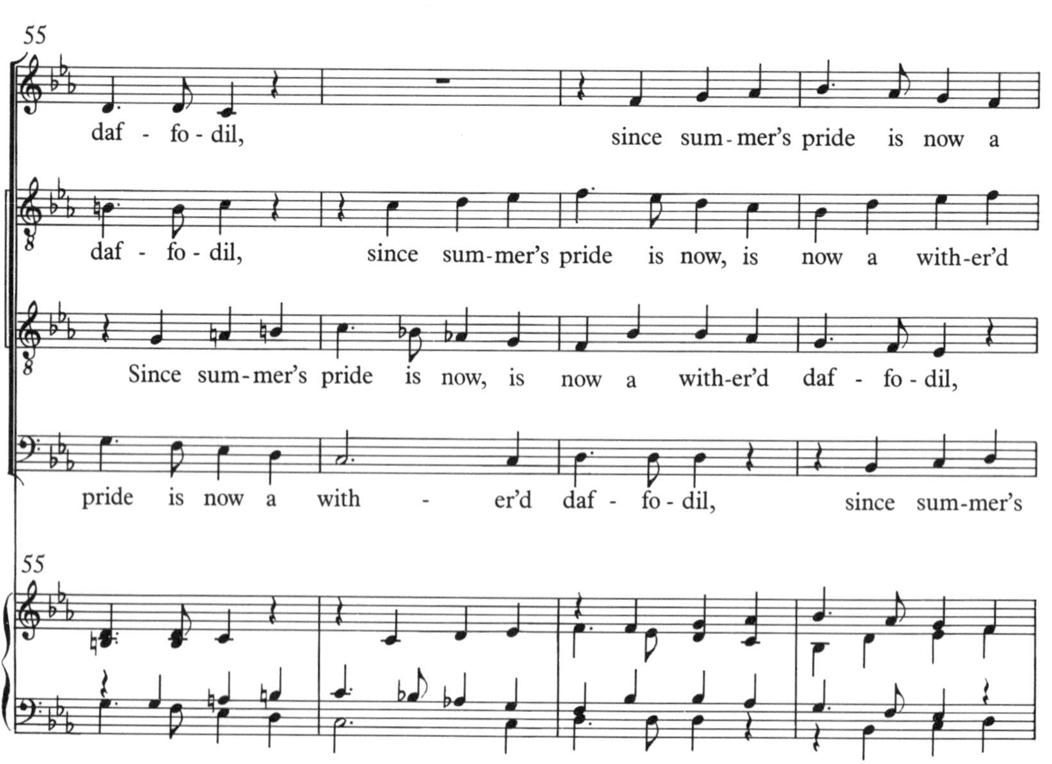
55
daf - fo - dil,
since sum-mer's pride is now a
daf - fo - dil,
since sum-mer's pride is now, is now a with-er'd
Since sum-mer's pride is now, is now a with-er'd daf - fo - dil,
pride is now a with - er'd daf - fo - dil,
since sum-mer's
55

59
with - er'd, with - er'd daf - fo - dil,
daf - fo - dil, since sum-mer's pride is now a with - er'd
since sum-mer's pride is now, is now a with-er'd daf - fo - dil,
pride a with-er'd daf - fo - dil, since sum-mer's pride is now a
59
63
since sum-mer's pride is now a with - - - -
daf - fo - dil, a with - er'd daf - fo - dil, since sum-mer's
a with-er'd daf - fo - dil, since sum-mer's pride is now a
with - er'd, with - er'd daf - fo - dil, a with - er'd
63

67
- er'd, with - - - -
pride is now a with - er'd, with - er'd daf - fo - dil, since sum-mer's
daf - fo - dil, since sum-mer's pride is now a daf - fo - dil,
daf - fo - dil, since sum-mer's pride is now a with - er'd,
67
71
- er'd, now a with - er'd daf - fo - dil.
pride is now, is now a with-er'd, with - - - er'd daf - fo - dil.
since sum-mer's pride is now a with - er'd, with - er'd daf - fo - dil.
with - - - - - - er'd daf - fo - dil.
71

14. O Poesy

NICHOLAS ROWE
(1674–1718)
(translated from Lucan's *Pharsalia*)

WILLIAM HORSLEY
(1774–1858)

9
[mf]
To thee bright Fame, to thee bright
[mf]
To thee bright Fame, to thee bright
Fame and length of days be - long, to thee bright Fame and length
days be - long, to thee bright Fame
length of days be - long, to thee bright Fame, bright
[mf]
To thee bright
9
13
cresc.
f
Fame and length of days be - long, to thee bright Fame and
cresc.
f
Fame and length of days be - long, bright
cresc.
f
of days be - long, to thee bright Fame and length of
f
and length of days be - long, to
cresc.
f
Fame and length of days, length of
cresc.
f
Fame and length of days, length of
13
cresc.
f

17
ff
1st time
2nd time
length of days be - long; - long:
Fame and length of days be - long; - long:
days, and length of days be - long; - long:
thee bright Fame and length of days be - long; - long:
days be - long; - long:
days be - long; - long:
21
f
Thou God - dess! thou E - ter - - ni -
Thou God - dess! thou E - ter - ni -
Thou God - dess! thou E - ter - - ni -
Thou God - dess! thou E - ter - ni -
Thou God - dess! thou E - ter - ni -
Thou God - dess! thou E - ter - ni -

27
mf
-ty canst give, And bid se - cure the mor - tal He - ro
[mf]
-ty canst give, And bid se - cure the mor - tal
-ty canst give,
[mf]
-ty canst give, And
-ty canst give,
-ty canst give,
27
mf
32
f
live, bid se - cure, se - cure the mor - tal He - ro live, Thou
He - ro live, the mor - tal He - ro live,
bid se - cure, se - cure the mor - tal He - ro live,
[mf]
f
And bid se - cure the mor - tal He - ro live, Thou
32
f

37
God - dess! thou E - ter - ni - ty canst
f
Thou God - dess! thou E - ter - ni - ty canst
f
Thou God - dess! thou E - ter - ni - ty canst
f
Thou God - dess! thou E - ter - ni - ty canst
God - dess! thou E - ter - ni - ty canst
f
Thou God - dess! thou E - ter - ni - ty canst
37
43
mf
give, And bid se - cure the mor - tal He - ro
mf
give, And bid se - cure the mor - tal
mf
give, And bid se - cure the
mf
give, And bid se -
give,
mf
give, And
43
mf

49
live, bid se-cure the mor - tal He - ro live, bid se-
He - ro live, bid se-cure the
mor-tal He-ro live, bid se-cure the mor - tal He - ro
-cure the He - ro live, bid se - cure the
mf
And bid se - cure, bid se-cure the mor - tal
bid se - cure the mor - tal He - ro live, the
49
54
cresc.
-cure the mor - tal He - ro live.
mor - tal, mor - tal He - ro live.
live, the mor - tal He - ro live.
mor - tal, mor - tal He - ro live.
He - ro live, the mor - tal he - ro live.
mor - tal, mor - tal He - ro live.
ff
54
cresc.
ff

15. Here in cool grot

WILLIAM SHENSTONE
(1714–63)

GARRET COLLEY WELLESLEY,
EARL OF MORNINGTON
(1735–81)

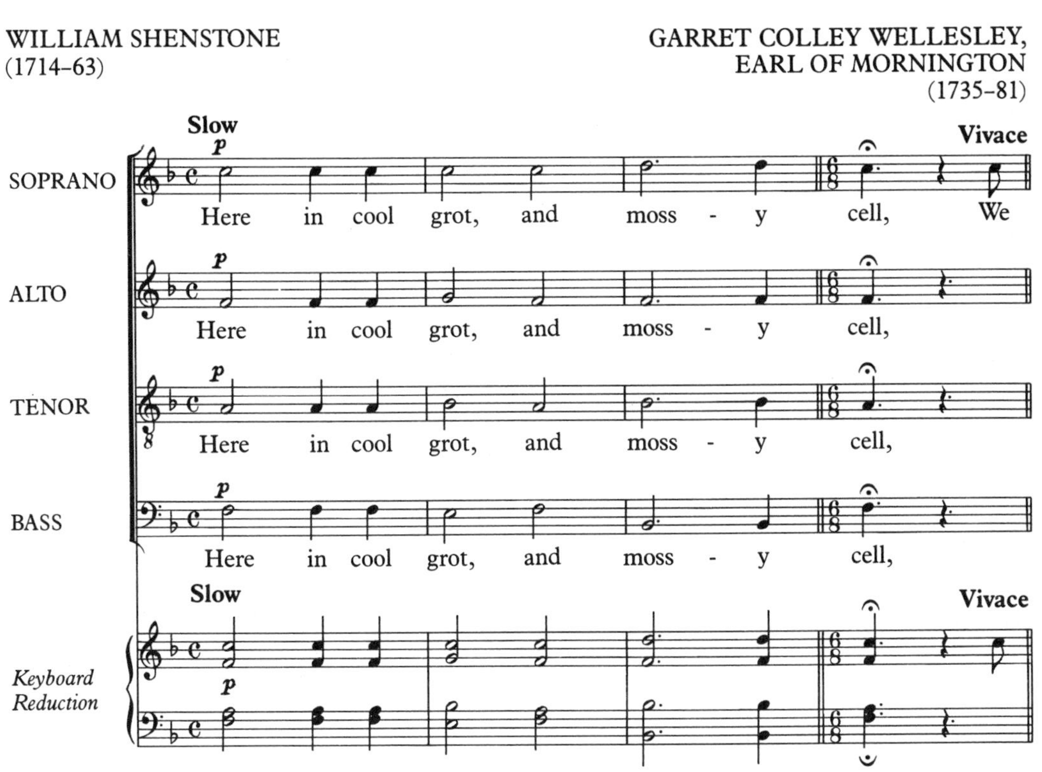

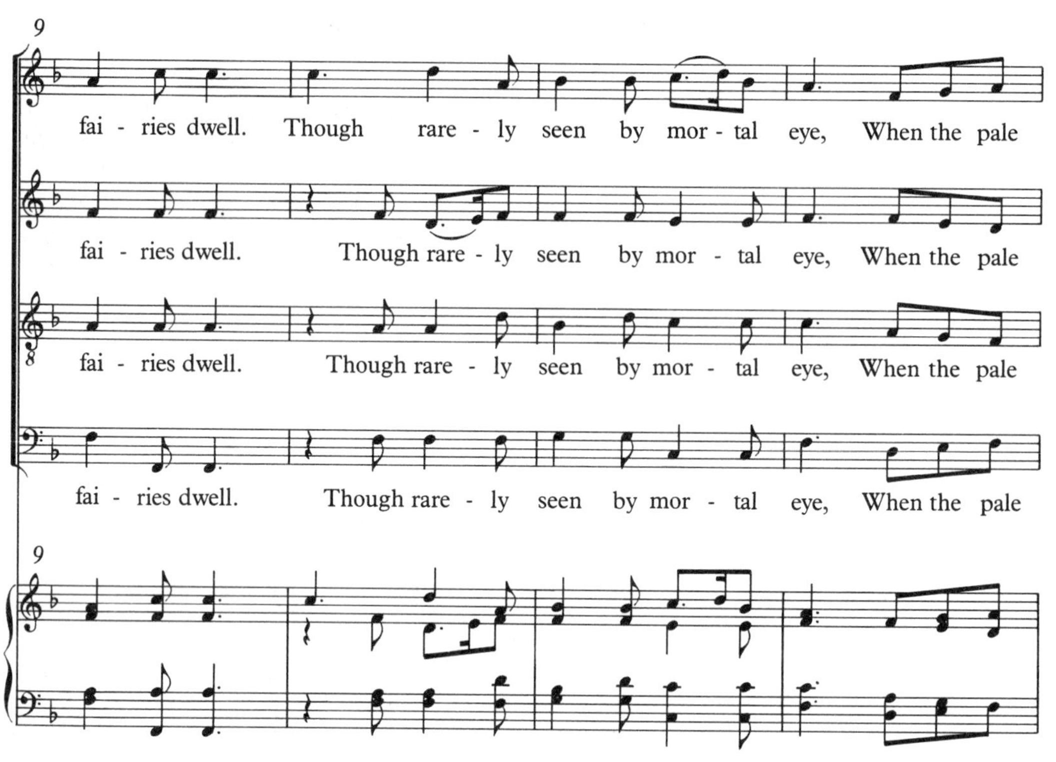
9
fai - ries dwell. Though rare - ly seen by mor - tal eye, When the pale
fai - ries dwell. Though rare - ly seen by mor - tal eye, When the pale
fai - ries dwell. Though rare - ly seen by mor - tal eye, When the pale
fai - ries dwell. Though rare - ly seen by mor - tal eye, When the pale
9

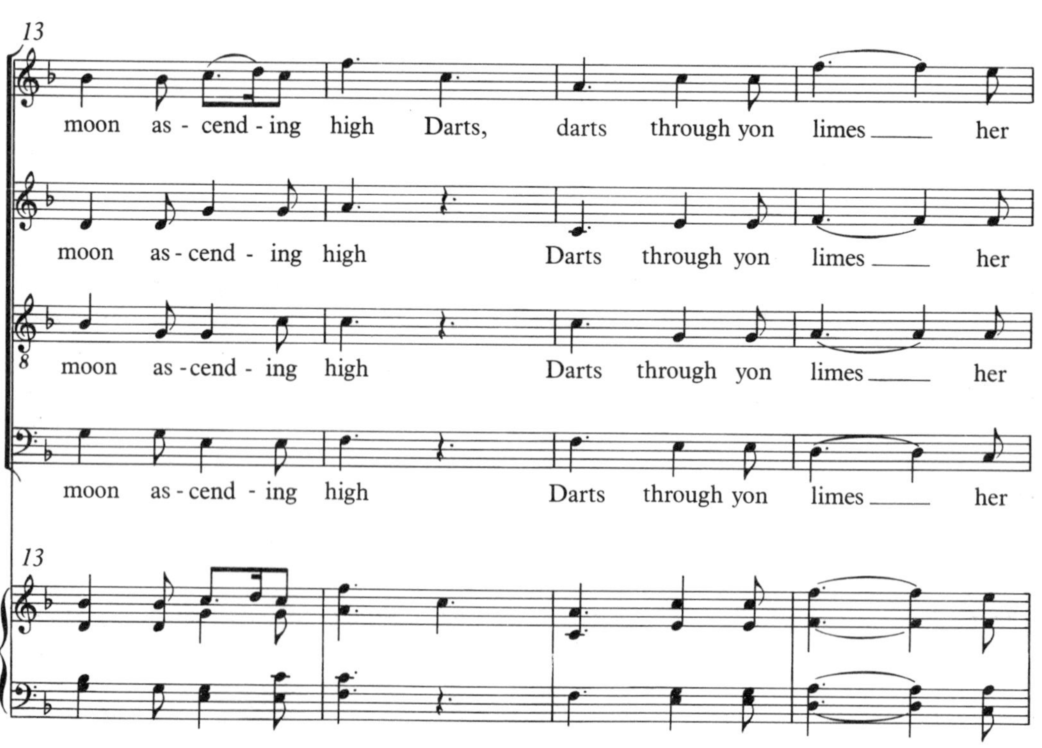
13
moon as - cend - ing high Darts, darts through yon limes her
moon as - cend - ing high Darts through yon limes her
moon as - cend - ing high Darts through yon limes her
moon as - cend - ing high Darts through yon limes her
13

17
qui -v'ring, qui - v'ring beams, We frisk it, frisk it, frisk it, frisk it, frisk it
qui -v'ring, qui - v'ring beams, We frisk it, frisk it, frisk it, frisk it
qui -v'ring, qui - v'ring beams, We frisk it, frisk it, frisk it, frisk it
qui -v'ring, qui - v'ring beams, We frisk it, frisk it, frisk it, frisk it
17

21
near these cry - stal streams, frisk it, frisk it, frisk it
near these cry - stal streams, frisk it, frisk it, frisk it
near these cry - stal streams, frisk it, frisk it, frisk it
near these cry - stal streams, frisk it, frisk it, frisk it
21

25
1st time
2nd time
near these cry - stal streams. We streams. Her beams re -
near these cry - stal streams. streams. Her beams re -
near these cry - stal streams. streams. Her beams re -
near these cry - stal streams. streams. Her beams re -
25
1st time
2nd time
29
- flect - ed from the wave, The
- flect - ed from the wave, Af - ford the light our re - vels crave, The
- flect - ed from the wave, Af - ford the light our re - vels crave, The
- flect - ed from the wave, our re - vels crave, The
29

33
turf, with dai - sies broi - dered o'er, Ex-ceeds, we wot, the
turf, with dai - sies broi - dered o'er, Ex - ceeds, we wot, the
turf, with dai - sies broi - dered o'er, Ex - ceeds, we wot, the
turf, with dai - sies broi - dered o'er, Ex - ceeds, we wot, the
33
38
Pa - rian floor;
Pa - rian floor; Nor yet for art - ful
Pa - rian floor; Nor
Pa - rian floor; Nor yet for art - ful strains we
38

42
Nor yet for art - ful strains we call, we call, we
strains, nor yet for art - ful strains we call, we call, we
yet for art - ful strains we call, we call, we call, we
call, for art - ful strains we call, we call, we call, we
42

46
[p]
call, But lis - ten, lis - ten, lis - ten,
call, But lis - ten, lis - ten, lis - ten,
call, But lis - ten, lis - ten, lis - ten,
call, But lis - ten, lis - ten, lis - ten,
46
[p]

50
lis-ten to the wa-ter's fall, lis-ten, lis-ten,
lis-ten to the wa-ter's fall, lis-ten, lis-ten,
lis-ten to the wa-ter's fall, lis-ten, lis-ten,
lis-ten to the wa-ter's fall, lis-ten, lis-ten,
50

55
1st time
2nd time
lis-ten, lis-ten to the wa-ter's fall. Her fall.
lis-ten, lis-ten to the wa-ter's fall. Her fall.
lis-ten, lis-ten to the wa-ter's fall. Her fall.
lis-ten, lis-ten to the wa-ter's fall. Her fall.
55
1st time
2nd time

16. Hail! hallowed fane!

(from lines written in Westminster Abbey)

ANON.

GARRET COLLEY WELLESLEY,
EARL OF MORNINGTON
(1735–81)

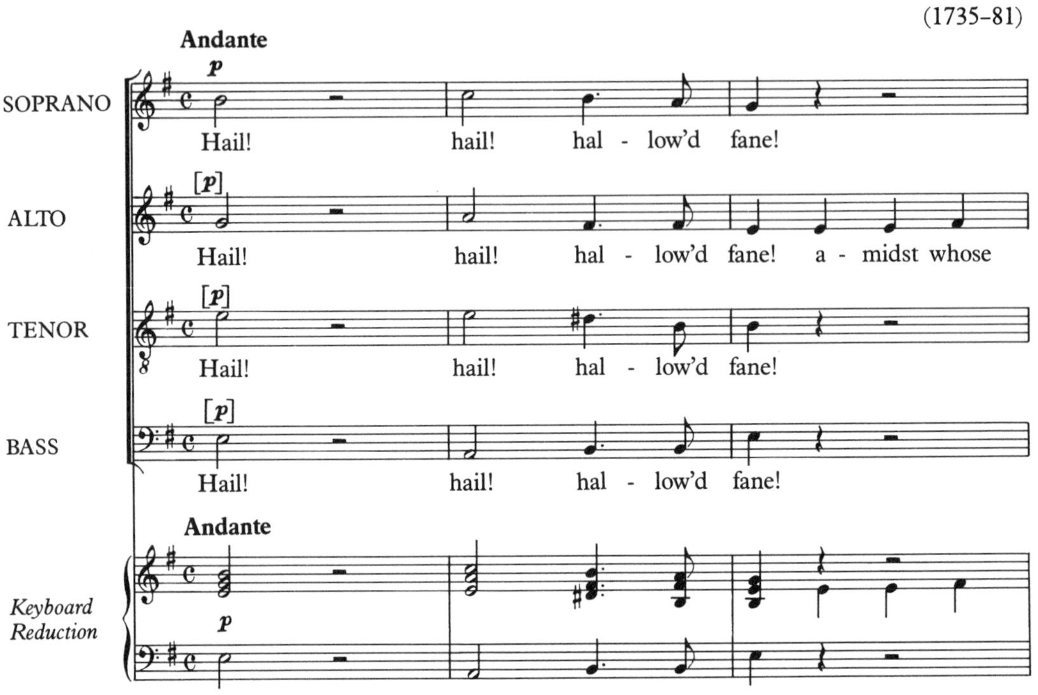

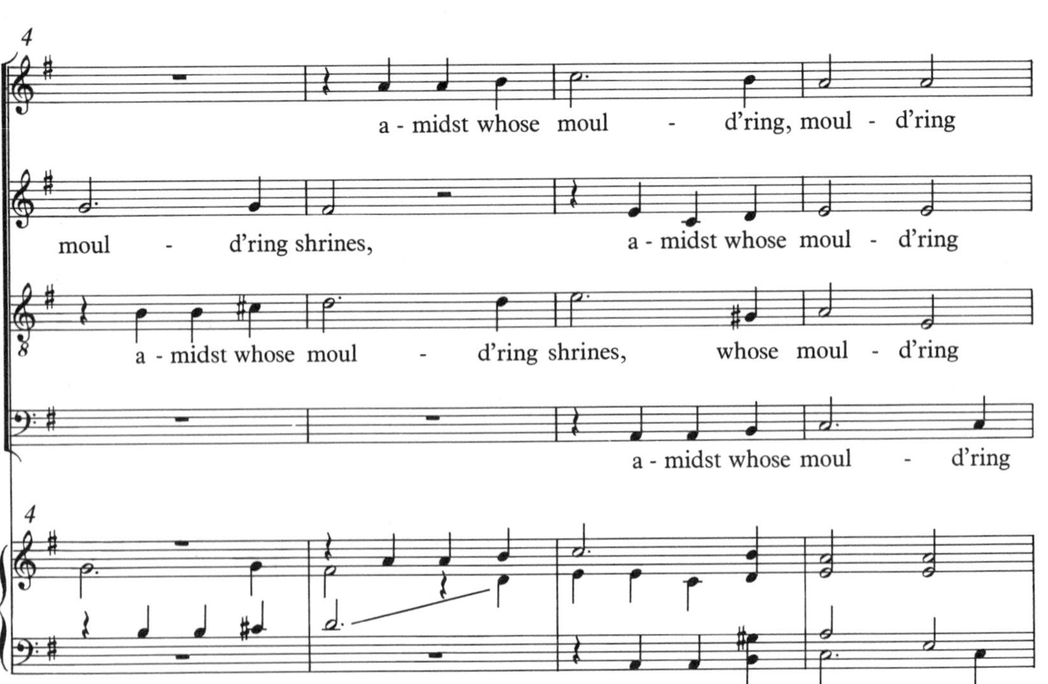

8
shrines Her vi - gils mu - sing me - lan - cho - ly
shrines Her vi - gils mu - sing me - lan - cho - ly
shrines Her vi - gils mu - sing me - lan - cho - ly
shrines Her vi - gils mu - sing me - lan - cho - ly
8

12
keeps; Up - on her arm her har - row'd, har - row'd
keeps; Up - on her arm her har - row'd, har - row'd
keeps; Up - on her arm her har - row'd
keeps; Up - on her arm her har - row'd
12

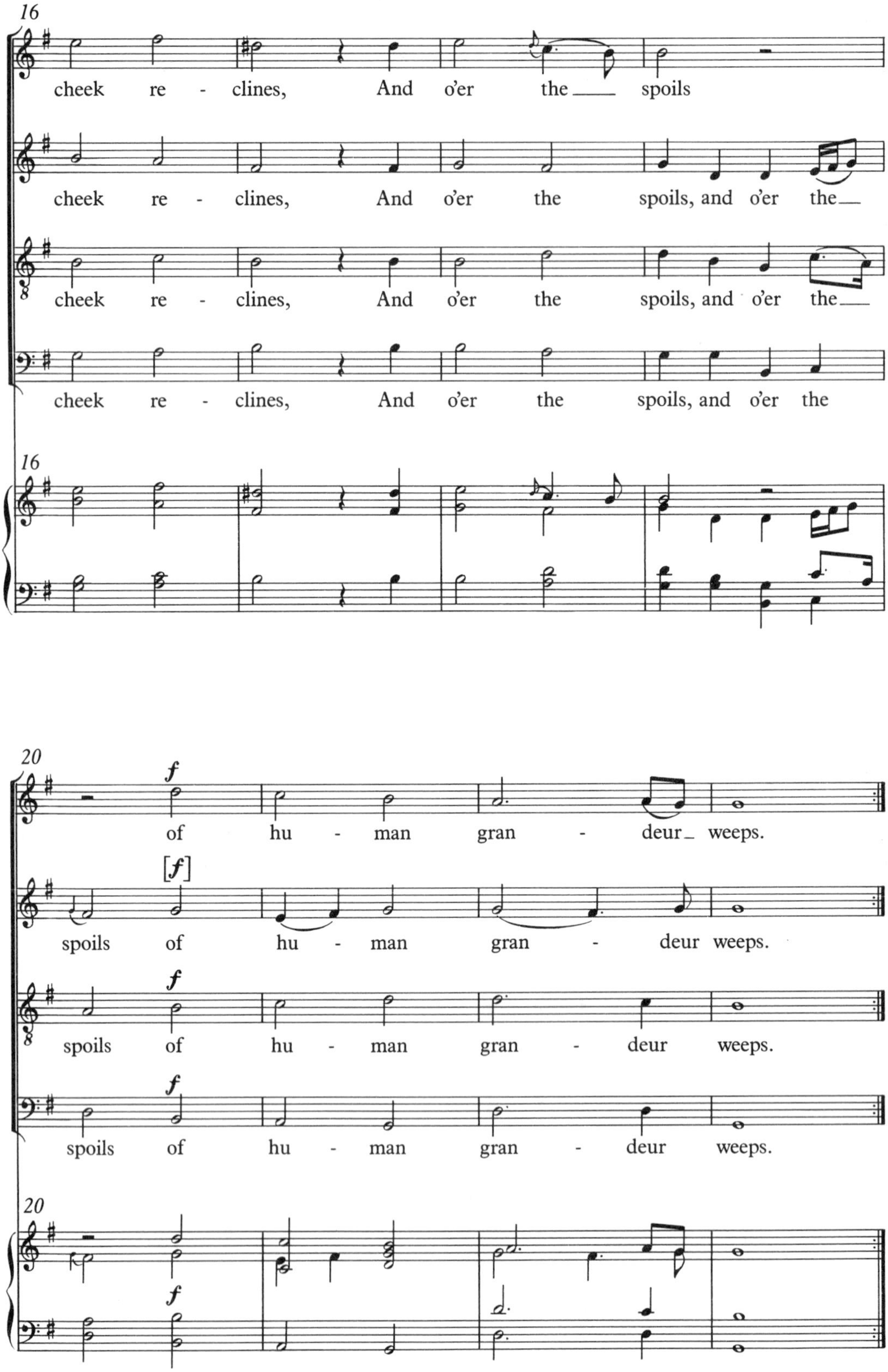

16

cheek re - clines, And o'er the ___ spoils

cheek re - clines, And o'er the spoils, and o'er the ___

cheek re - clines, And o'er the spoils, and o'er the ___

cheek re - clines, And o'er the spoils, and o'er the

16

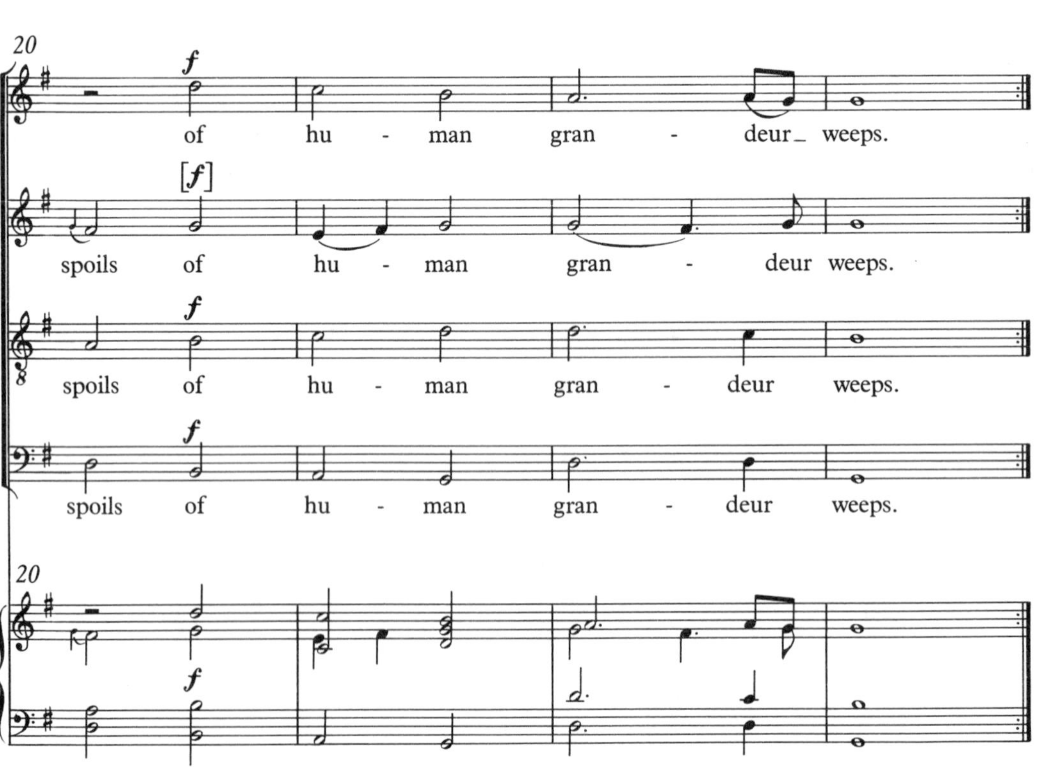

24
f
Hail! aw - ful e - di - fice! thine aisles a - long, In con - tem -
f
Hail! aw - ful e - di - fice! thine aisles a - long, In con - tem -
[f]
Hail! aw - ful e - di - fice! thine aisles a - long,
f
Hail! aw - ful e - di - fice! thine aisles a - long,
24
f

28
- pla - tion wrapt, O let me stray, in
- pla - tion wrapt, O let me, let me stray, in
In con - tem - pla - tion wrapt, O let me stray, in
In con - tem - pla - tion wrapt, O let me stray, in
28

32
con - tem - pla - tion wrapt, O let me, let me stray;
con - tem - pla - tion wrapt, O let me, let me stray;
con - tem - pla - tion wrapt, O let me, let me stray;
con - tem - pla - tion wrapt, O let me, let me stray; And,
p
32
p

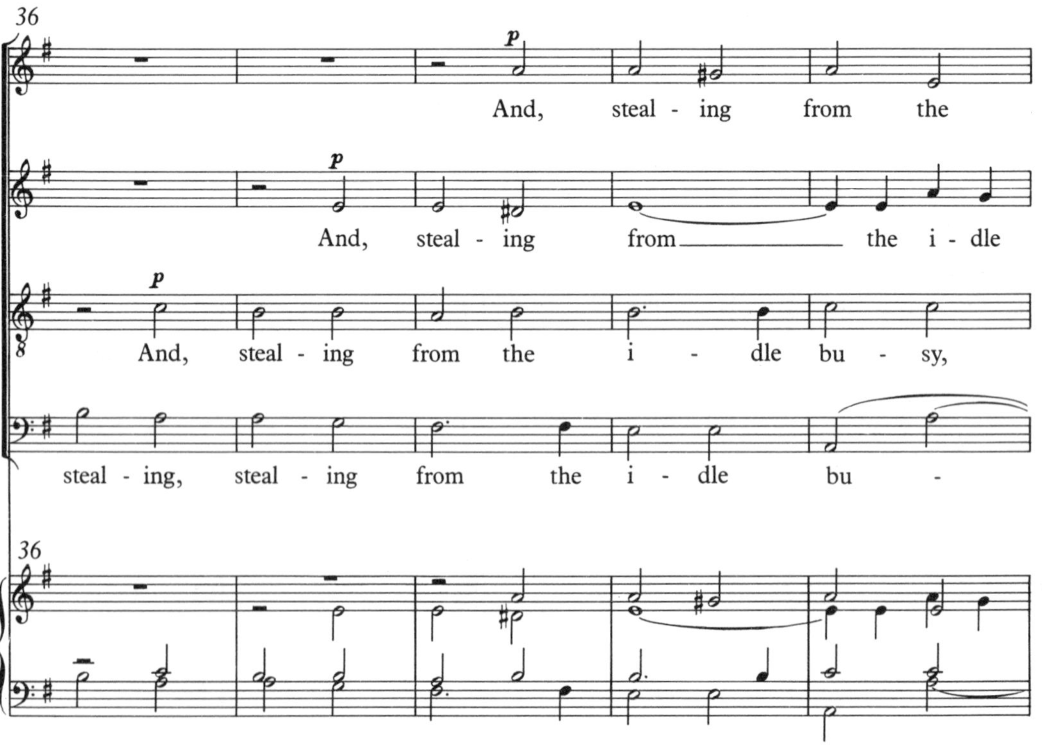
36
p
And, steal - ing from the
p
And, steal - ing from the i - dle
p
And, steal - ing from the i - dle bu - sy,
steal - ing, steal - ing from the i - dle bu -
36

41
i - dle bu - sy throng, Se - rene - ly me - di - tate the
bu - sy throng, Se - rene - ly me - di - tate the
bu - sy throng, Se - rene - ly me - di - tate the
- - sy throng, Se - rene - ly me - di - tate the
41

45
Grazioso
mo - ral lay. What plea - sing sad - ness
mo - ral lay. What plea - sing sad - ness
mo - ral lay. What plea - sing sad - ness
mo - ral lay. What plea - sing sad - ness
45
Grazioso

49
fills my thought-ful breast When - e'er my steps these
fills my thought-ful breast When - e'er my steps these
fills my thought-ful breast When - e'er my steps these
fills my thought-ful breast When - e'er my steps these
49

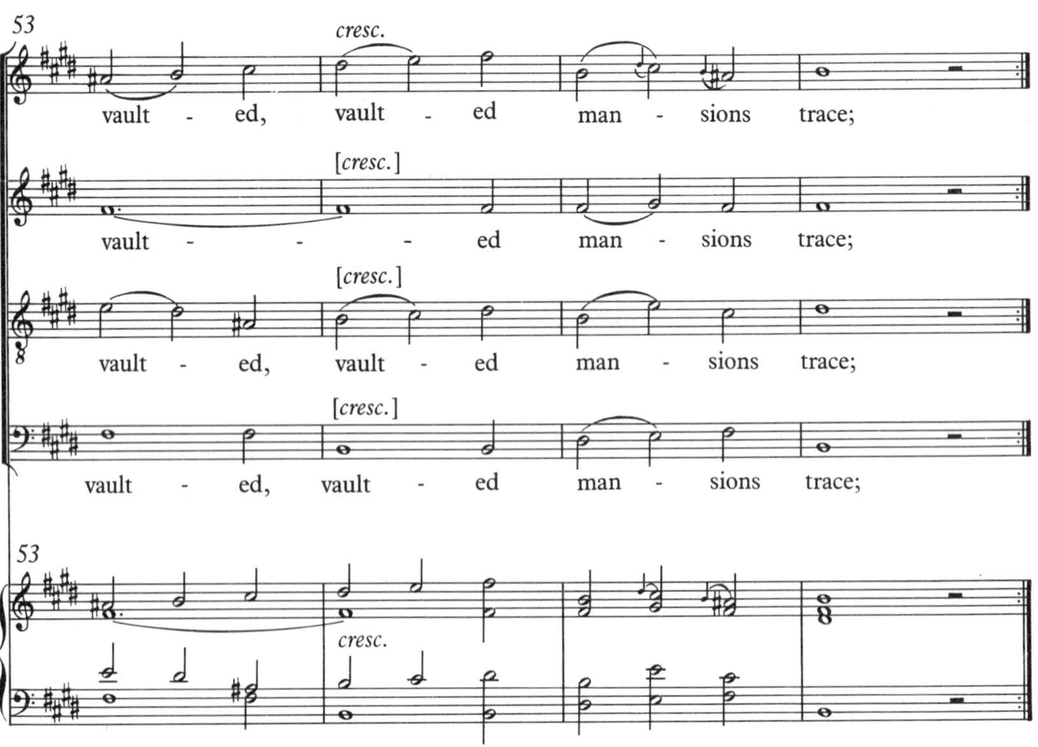
53
cresc.
vault - ed, vault - ed man - sions trace;
[cresc.]
vault - - - ed man - sions trace;
[cresc.]
vault - ed, vault - ed man - sions trace;
[cresc.]
vault - ed, vault - ed man - sions trace;
53
cresc.

57
p
Where, in their si - lent tombs, for e - ver rest
p
Where, in their si - lent tombs, for e - ver rest
p
Where, in their si - lent tombs, for e - ver rest
p
f
Where, in their si - lent tombs, for e - ver rest The
57
p
f
62
f
The ho - nor'd ash - es of the Bri - tish race.
f
The ho - nor'd ash - es of the Bri - tish race.
f
The ho - nor'd ash - es of the Bri - tish race.
ho - nor'd ash - es of the Bri - tish race.
62

17. Elegy for Cymbeline

SHAKESPEARE
(1564–1616)
(*Cymbeline*, IV. ii)

JAMES NARES
(1715–83)

9
gone to take thy wa - ges, Fear no more the heat of the
gone to take thy wa - ges, Fear no more the heat of the
gone to take thy wa - ges, Fear no more the heat of the
9
12
sun, Nor the fu - rious win-ter's ra - ges, nor the
sun, Nor the fu - rious win-ter's ra - ges, the
sun, Nor the fu - rious win - ter's, the fu - rious win - ter's
12
14
fu - rious win-ter's ra - ges, the fu - rious win-ter's ra - ges, the
fu - rious win-ter's ra - ges, the fu - rious win-ter's ra - ges, the
ra - ges, the fu - rious win-ter's ra - ges, the fu - rious win - ter's
14

16
pp
fu - rious_ win - ter's_ ra - ges; Thou thy world - ly_
fu - rious_ win - ter's_ ra - ges; Thou thy world - ly
ra - ges; Thou thy world - ly
18
task_ hast_ done,_ Home art gone to take thy_ wa - ges.
task hast_ done,_ Home art gone to take thy_ wa - ges.
task hast done, Home art gone to take thy wa - ges.
21 Larghetto
mf
Gold - en lads_ and lass - es must_ All fol - low thee_ and
Gold - en lads_ and lass - es must_ All fol - low thee_ and
Gold - en lads_ and lass - es must All_ fol - low thee and

24
p
pp
turn to dust, all fol - low thee, all turn to dust,
turn to dust, all fol - low thee, all turn to dust,
turn to dust, all fol - low thee, all turn to dust,
27
f
Gold - en lads and lass - es must All fol - low thee and
Gold - en lads and lass - es must All fol - low thee and
Gold - en lads and lass - es must All fol - low thee and
30
turn to dust, all fol - low thee, and turn to dust,
turn to dust, all fol - low thee, and turn to dust,
turn to dust, all fol - low thee and turn to dust,

33
Gold-en lads_and lass - es must_ All_ fol-low thee_ and turn to_dust._
Gold-en lads_and lass - es must_ All_ fol-low thee_ and turn to_dust._
Gold - en lads_and lass-es must All fol-low thee and turn to dust.
37 Largo Bass Solo [mf]
No Ex - or - ci - ser harm thee, nor no witch-craft
39
charm thee. Ghosts un - laid for - bear_thee, no-thing ill come near_thee.
42 [Andante]
Qui - et,_ qui - et_ con-sum-ma-tion have,_ Un - re - mo - ved
Qui - et,_ qui - et_ con - sum-ma-tion have,_ Un - re - mo - ved
p (Full)
Qui - et, qui - et con - sum-ma - tion have, Un - re - mo - ved

45
be thy grave, un-re-mo-ved be thy grave,
be thy grave, un-re-mo-ved be thy grave,
be thy grave, un-re-mo-ved be thy grave,
45
48
Qui-et, qui-et con-sum-ma-tion have, Un-re-mo-ved
Qui-et, qui-et con-sum-ma-tion have, Un-re-mo-ved
Qui-et, qui-et con-sum-ma-tion have, Un-re-mo-ved
48
51
be thy grave, un-re-mo-ved be thy grave.
be thy grave, un-re-mo-ved be thy grave.
be thy grave, un-re-mo-ved be thy grave.
51

18. Poor Barbara

SHAKESPEARE
(1564–1616)
(*Othello*, IV. iii)

WILLIAM SHIELD
(1748–1829)

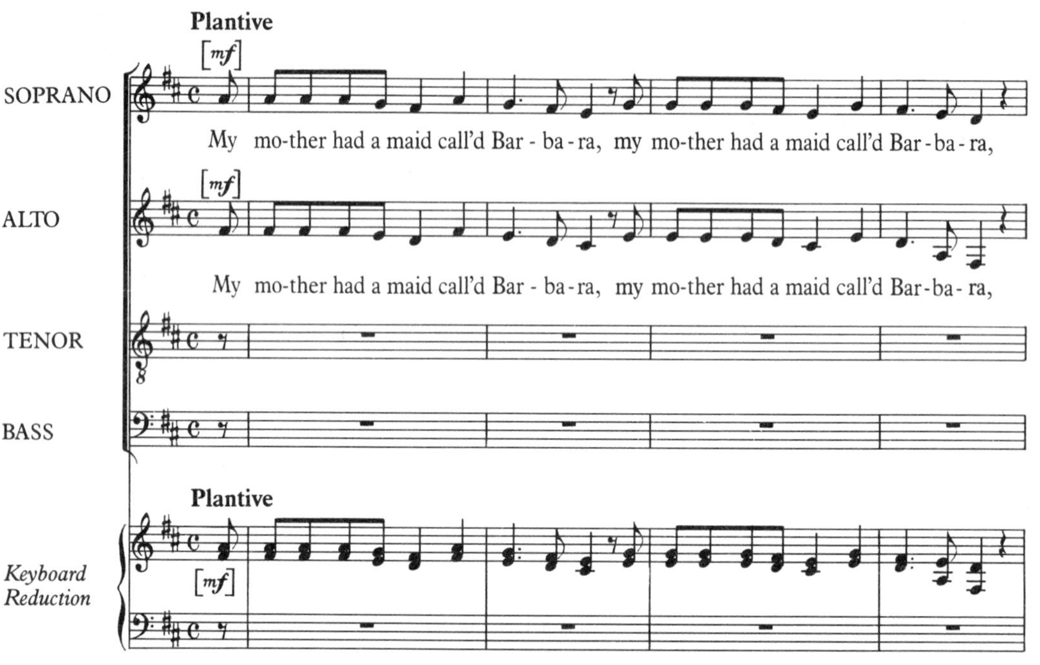

10
[p]
false and did for - sake her, and he she lov'd prov'd false and did for - sake her.
[p]
false and did for - sake her, he she lov'd prov'd false and did for - sake her.
[p]
false and did for - sake her, he she lov'd prov'd false and did for - sake her.
[p]
false and did for - sake her, he she lov'd prov'd false and did for - sake her.
10
[p]
15
[mf]
She had a song of wil - low; an old thing 'twas, but it ex-press'd her
[mf]
She had a song of wil - low; an old thing 'twas, but it ex-press'd her
[mf]
an old thing 'twas, but it ex-press'd her
[mf]
She had a song of wil - low; an old thing 'twas, but it ex-press'd her
15
[mf]

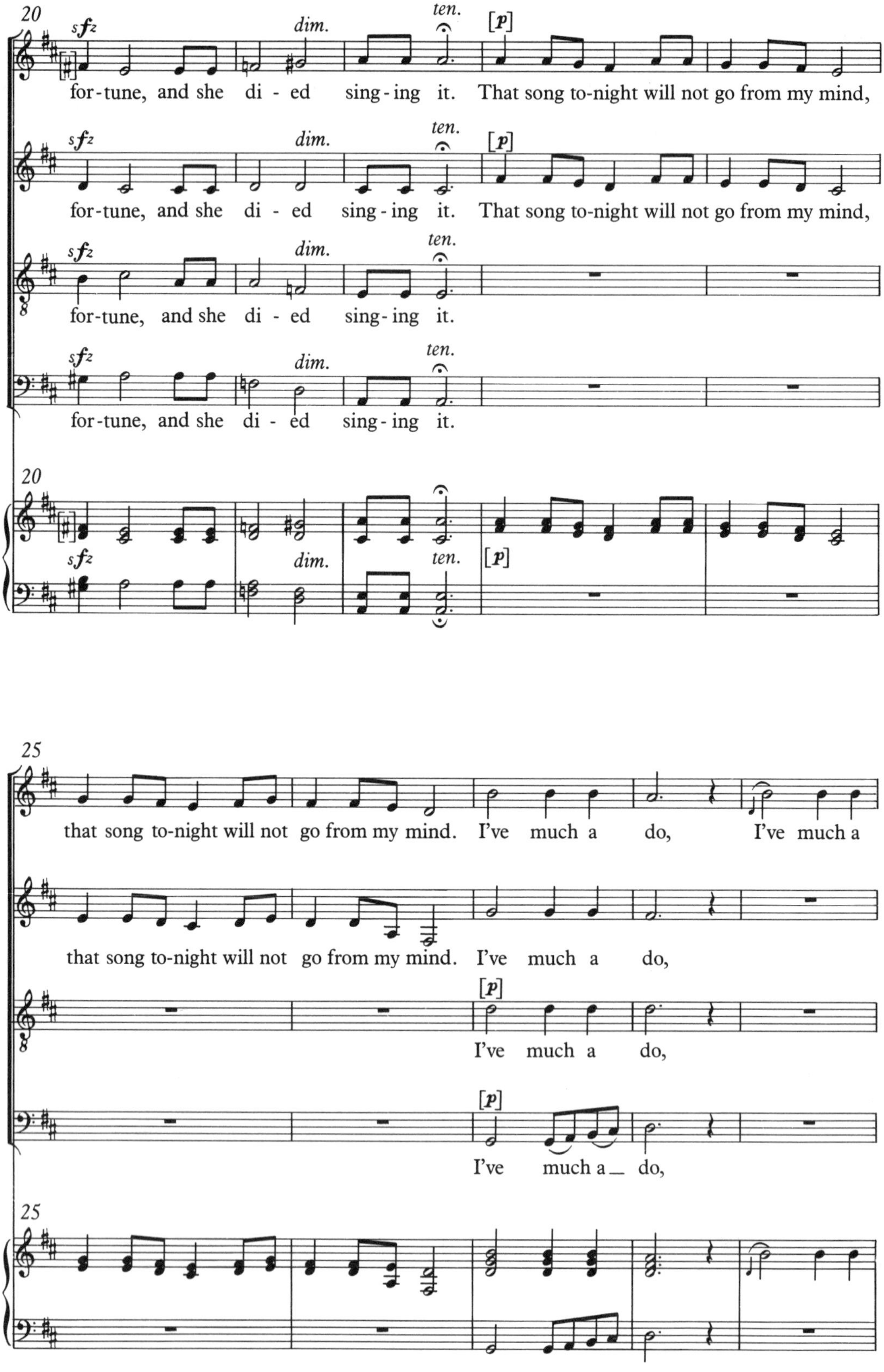

20

sfz *dim.* *ten.* [*p*]

for-tune, and she di - ed sing - ing it. That song to-night will not go from my mind,

sfz *dim.* *ten.* [*p*]

for-tune, and she di - ed sing - ing it. That song to-night will not go from my mind,

sfz *dim.* *ten.*

for-tune, and she di - ed sing - ing it.

sfz *dim.* *ten.*

for-tune, and she di - ed sing - ing it.

20

sfz *dim.* *ten.* [*p*]

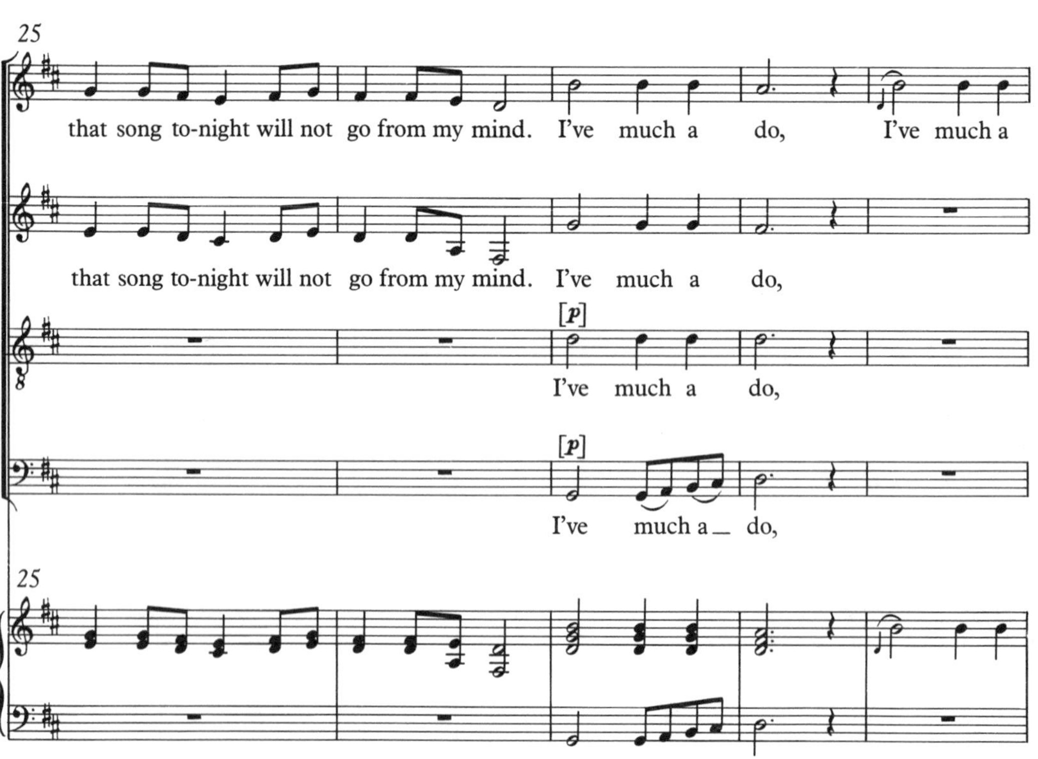

30
do not to go hang my head all o' one side and sing it like poor
And sing it like poor
And sing it like poor
And sing it like poor
30
34
[pp]
Bar - ba - ra, poor Bar - ba - ra, poor Bar - ba - ra.
Bar - ba - ra, poor Bar - ba - ra, poor Bar - ba - ra.
Bar - ba - ra, poor Bar - ba - ra, poor Bar - ba - ra.
Bar - ba - ra, poor Bar - ba - ra, poor Bar - ba - ra.
34

19. Merrily push round the glass

Text as reported in Washington Irving (1783–1859): *Tales of a Traveller*

WILLIAM SHORE (1791–1877)

11
rit.
Mer-ri - ly, mer-ri - ly fud - dle thy nose, Un - til it right ro - sy shall
Mer - ri - ly, mer - ri - ly fud - dle thy nose, Un - til it right ro - sy shall
11
rit.
14
a tempo
be.
be.
For a jol - ly red _ nose, I speak un - der the rose, _ 'Tis a
14
a tempo
17
tr
sign of good com - pa - ny, 'tis a sign of good com - pa - ny. Then
17
tr

21
f
Mer - ri - ly, mer - ri - ly push round the glass And mer - ri - ly troll the
[f]
Mer - ri - ly, mer - ri - ly push round the glass And mer - ri - ly troll the
[f]
mer - ri - ly, mer - ri - ly push round the glass And mer - ri - ly troll the
21
f
24
glee, For he who won't drink 'till he wink is an ass; So
glee, For he who won't drink 'till he wink is an ass; So
glee, For he who won't drink 'till he wink is an ass; So
24
27
neigh-bour I'll drink to thee, to thee, so neigh-bour I'll drink to thee.
neigh-bour I'll drink to thee, to thee, so neigh-bour I'll drink to thee.
neigh-bour I'll drink to thee, to thee, so neigh-bour I'll drink to thee.
27

20. Ring out ye crystal spheres

JOHN MILTON
(*c.*1563–1647)

JOHN STAFFORD SMITH
(1750–1836)

7
touch our sen - ses so) And let your sil - ver chime Move in me-lo-dious
touch our sen - ses so) And let your sil - ver chime Move in me-lo-dious
touch our sen - ses so)
touch our sen - ses so)
touch our sen - ses so)
7
T[asto] S[olo]
6
6 4
5 ♯
10
time;
time;
And let your sil - ver
And let your sil - ver
And let your sil - ver
And let the bass of heav'ns deep or - gan blow,
And let the bass of heav'ns deep or - gan blow,
10
Ped.

13
chime Move in me-lo-dious time;
chime Move in me-lo-dious time;
chime Move in me-lo-dious time;
and let the bass of heav'ns deep or - gan
and let the bass of heav'ns deep or - gan
13
tr
16
And let your sil-ver chime Move in me-lo-dious time, And with your
And let your sil-ver chime Move in me-lo-dious time, And with your,
And let your sil-ver chime Move in me-lo-dious time, And with your,
blow,
blow,
16
Ped.

19

nine - fold har - mo - ny, your nine - fold har-mo-ny Make up full

your nine, your nine - fold, nine - fold har-mo-ny Make up full

your nine - fold, nine - fold har-mo-ny Make up

your nine - fold, nine - fold har-mo-ny Make up full

your nine - fold har-mo-ny Make up full

19

6 7/5 6/4 5

22

con - sort to th'an - ge - lic sym-pho-ny, make up full

con - sort to th'an - ge - lic sym-pho-ny, make up full

full con-sort to th'an - ge - lic sym-pho-ny, make up full

con - sort to th'an - ge - lic sym-pho-ny, make up full

con - sort to th'an - ge - lic sym-pho-ny, make up full

22

6/5 9/7 8/6 5 7/♯ 6/4 5/4 ♯ 6 6

25
con - - - - - sort to th'an-ge - -
con - - - - sort to th'an - ge - -
con - - - - sort to th'an - ge - -
con - - - sort to th'an - ge - -
con - - - sort to th'an - ge - -
28
[mf]
- - - - - - lic sym-pho-ny. For if such ho - ly
- - - - - lic sym-pho-ny. For if such ho - ly
- - - lic sym-pho-ny. For if such ho - ly
- - - - - lic sym-pho-ny. For if such ho - ly
- - - - - lic sym-pho-ny. For if such ho - ly

31

Song En-wrap our fan-cy long, Time will run back, and fetch the age — of

Song En-wrap our fan-cy long,

Song En-wrap our fan-cy long, Time will run back, and fetch the age — of

Song En-wrap our fan-cy long,

Song En-wrap our fan-cy long, Time will run back, and fetch the age of

31

6 6 5 8 4 ♯ 6 7 5 6 6/4 5/♯

34

gold, time will run back, and fetch the age of — gold,

Time will run back, and fetch the age of gold, the age — of — gold,

gold, time will run back, and fetch the age of gold,

Time will run back, and fetch the age of gold, time —

gold, time will run back, and fetch the age of gold, time will run

34

6 7 ♯ 6 7 4 ♯ 6 6 6/5 6/4 5/♯ 6

37
time will run back, and fetch the age of gold, And
time will run back, and fetch the age of gold, And
time will run back, run back, and fetch the age of gold, And
will run back, run back, and fetch the age of gold, And
back, will run back, run back, and fetch the age of gold, And
37
7 ♯ 7 6 9 8 ♯ ♯ ♯ 5 ♯ ♯
7 6 4
40
Slow
speck-l'd, speck-l'd va-ni-ty will sick-en, sick-en soon and
speck-l'd, speck-l'd va-ni-ty will sick-en, sick-en soon and
speck-l'd, speck-l'd va-ni-ty will sick-en, sick-en soon and
speck-l'd, speck-l'd va-ni-ty will sick-en, sick-en soon and
speck-l'd, speck-l'd va-ni-ty will sick-en, sick-en soon and
40
Slow
♮7 5

42
f
p
pp
die, And lep - rous sin will melt, melt from
dim.
die, And lep - rous sin will melt, melt from
die, And lep - rous sin will melt, melt from
die, And lep - rous sin will melt, melt from
die, And lep - rous sin will melt, melt from
45
Andante
earth - ly mould, And Hell it - self will pass a -
earth - ly mould, And Hell it - self will pass a -
earth - ly mould, And Hell it - self will pass a -
earth - ly mould, And Hell it - self will pass a -
earth - ly mould, And Hell it - self will pass a -

48
- way, will pass a - way,
- way, will pass a - way,
- way, will pass a - way, And leave her do - lo - rous
- way, will pass a - way And leave her do - lo - rous
- way, will pass a - way,
48
6 6 4 3
51
to the freez - ing day, And Hell it -
to the freez - ing day, And Hell it -
man - sions, And Hell it -
man - sions, And Hell it -
to the freez - ing day, And Hell it -
51
5♮ 5 6 ♮ 5 3

54
p
f
-self will pass a - way, and Hell it - self will pass a -
-self will pass a - way, and Hell it - self will pass a -
-self will pass a - way, and Hell it - self will pass a -
-self will pass a - way, and Hell it - self will pass a -
-self will pass a - way, and Hell it - self will pass a -
54
5 6
♮3
6 7
57
- way, And leave her
- way, will pass a - way, And leave her
- way, will pass a - way, And leave her
- way, will pass a - way, And leave her
- way, will pass a - way, And leave, and leave her
57
6 6 6 6 3 3 3 5 6 5

60
do - lo - rous man - sions to the freez - ing
do - lo-rous man - sions to the freez - ing
do - lo-rous man - sions to the freez - ing
do - lo - rous man - sions to the freez - ing
do - lo - rous man - sions to the freez - ing
60
6 6 6 6 6 6
64
dim.
day, the freez-ing day, the freez-ing day.
dim.
day.
dim.
day, the freez - ing day.
p dim.
day, the freez-ing day, the freez-ing day.
dim.
day, the freez-ing day.
64
p
dim.
♮5
5
♮4 3

21. Under the greenwood tree

SHAKESPEARE
(1564–1616)
(*As you like it*, II. v)

JOHN STAFFORD SMITH
(1750–1836)

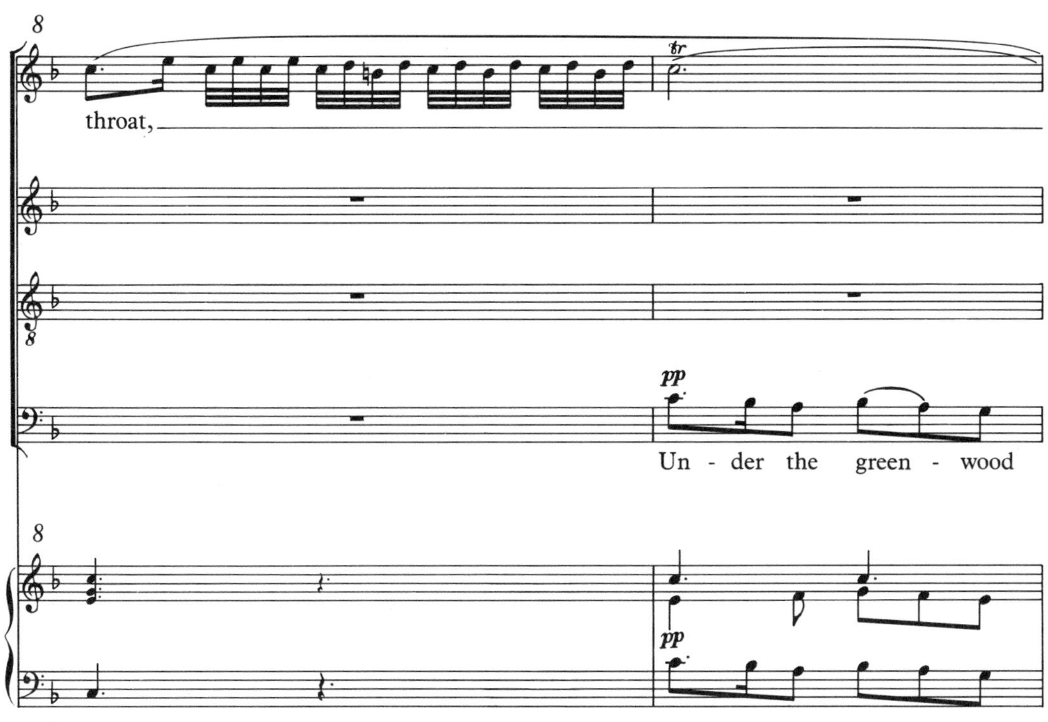
8
throat,
pp
Un - der the green - wood
8
pp
pp

10
pp
Un - der the green - wood tree,
pp
Un - der the green - wood tree, the green - wood tree, Who loves to
tree, the green - wood tree, the green - wood tree, Who
10

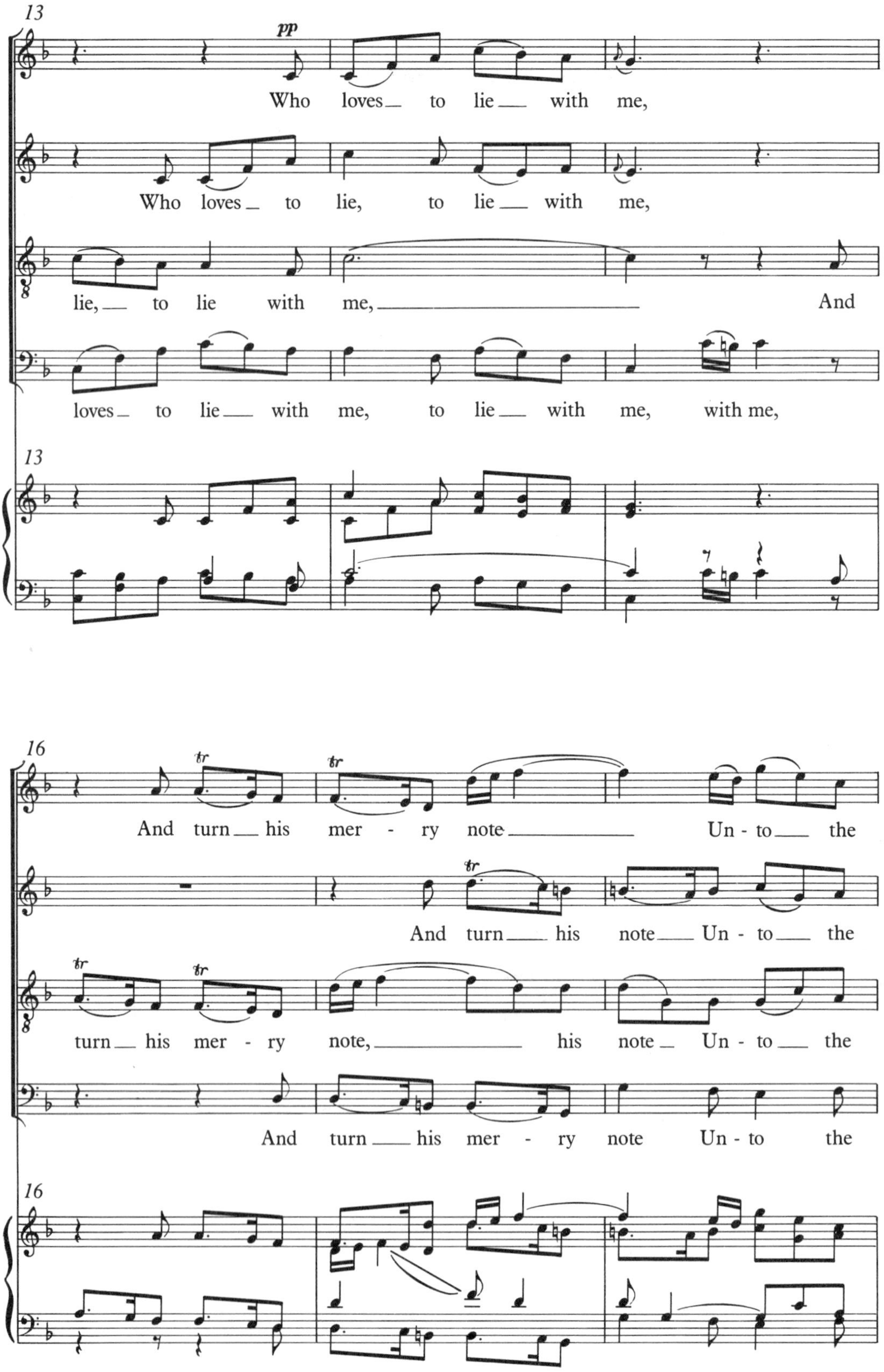

13

pp

Who loves to lie with me,

Who loves to lie, to lie with me,

lie, to lie with me, And

loves to lie with me, to lie with me, with me,

13

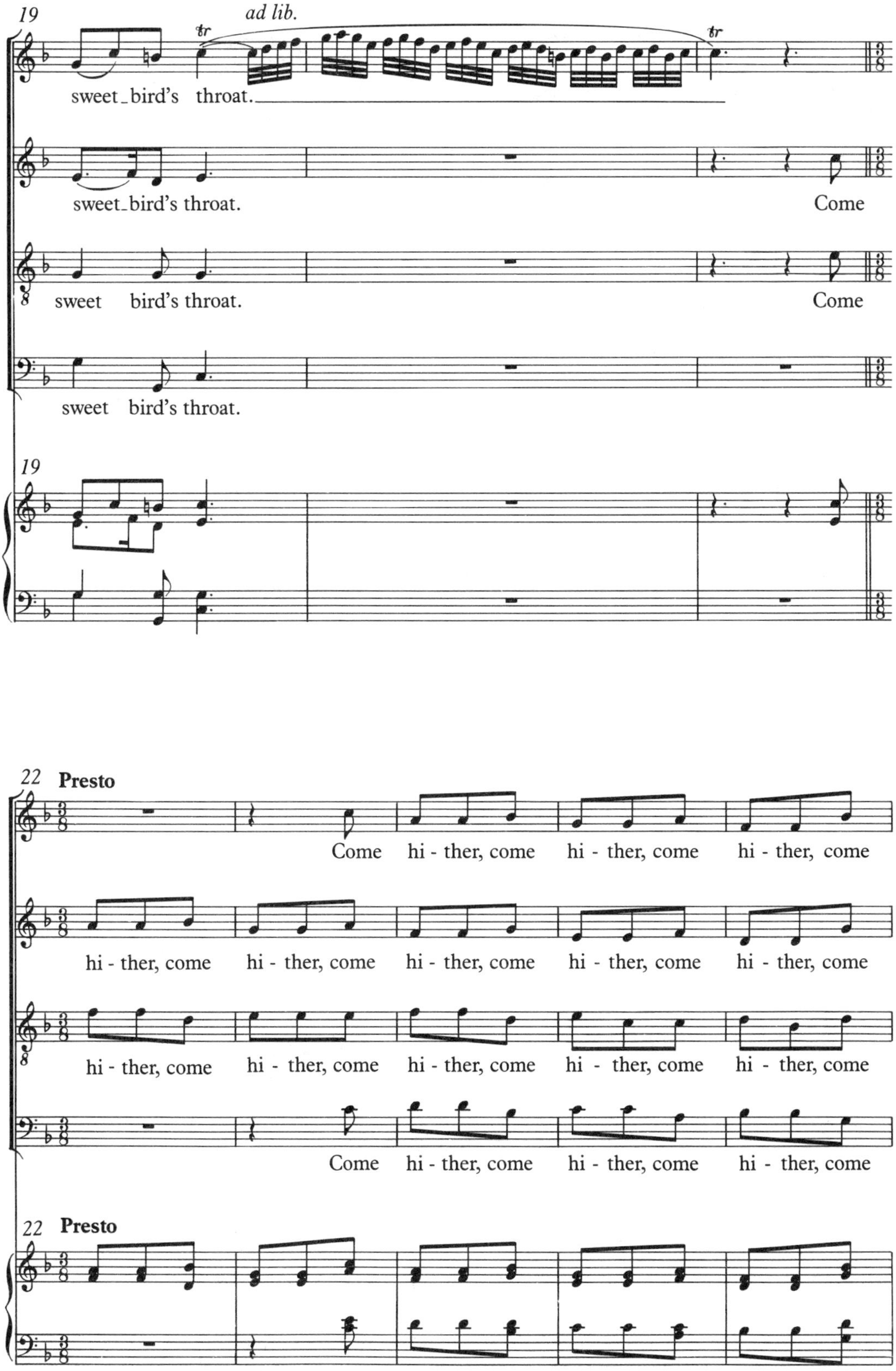

19 *ad lib.*

sweet_bird's throat.

sweet_bird's throat. Come

sweet bird's throat. Come

sweet bird's throat.

19

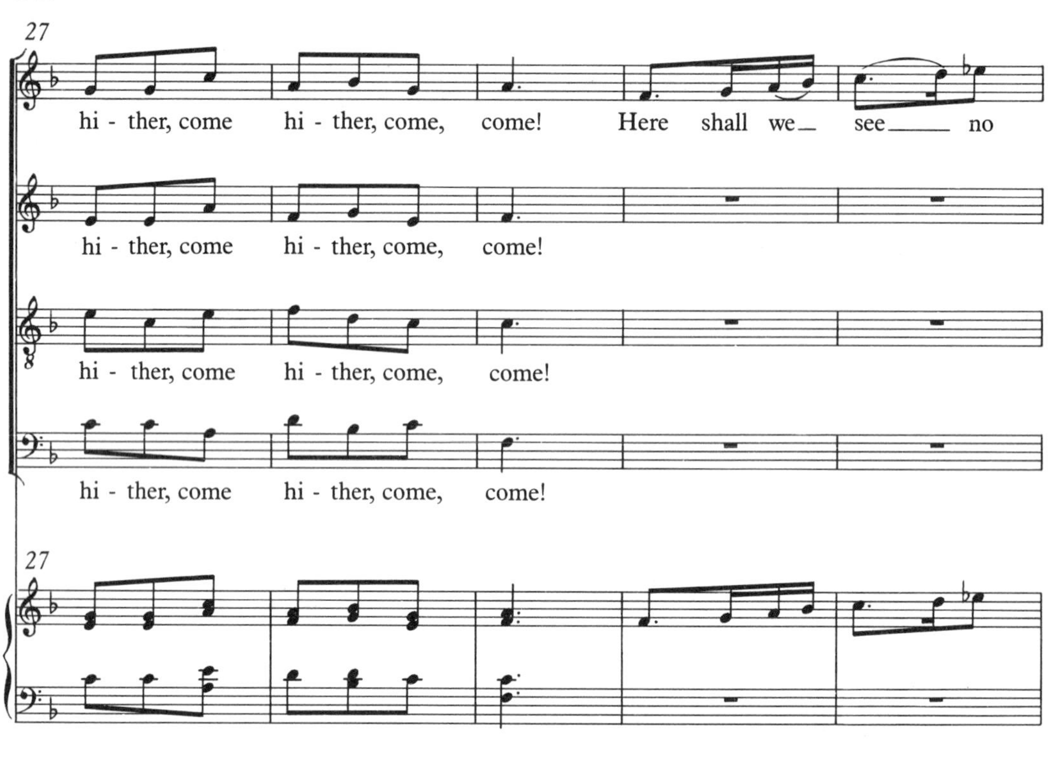
27
hi - ther, come hi - ther, come, come! Here shall we see no
hi - ther, come hi - ther, come, come!
hi - ther, come hi - ther, come, come!
hi - ther, come hi - ther, come, come!
27

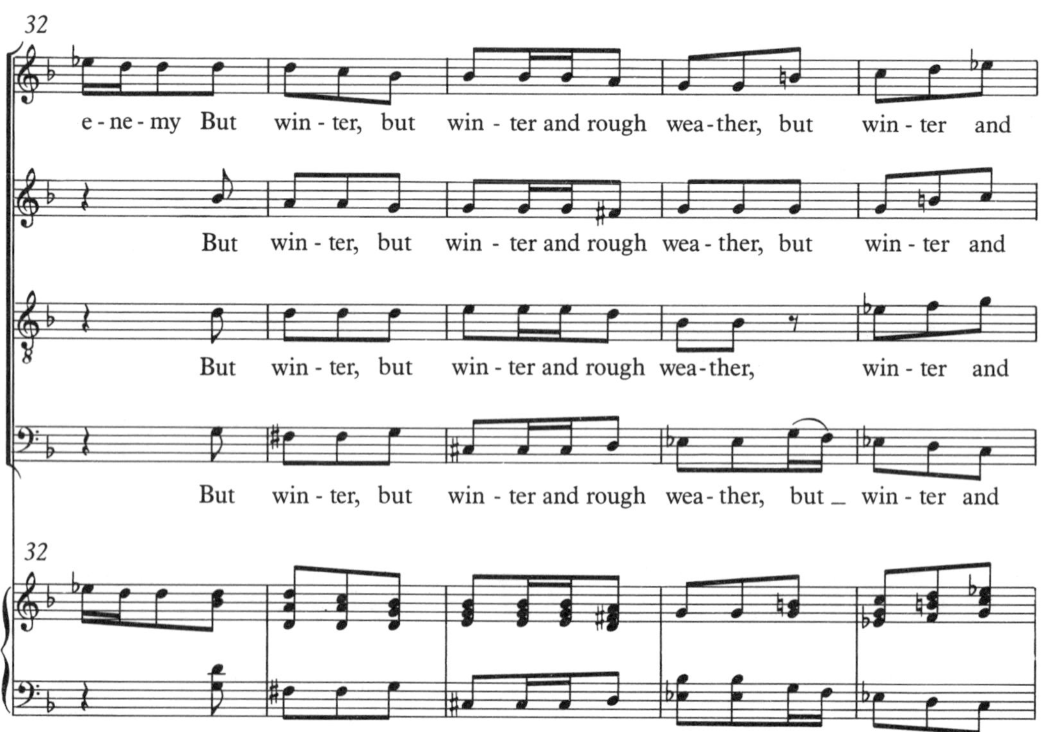
32
e - ne - my But win - ter, but win - ter and rough wea - ther, but win - ter and
But win - ter, but win - ter and rough wea - ther, but win - ter and
But win - ter, but win - ter and rough wea - ther, win - ter and
But win - ter, but win - ter and rough wea - ther, but win - ter and
32

37
rough, rough wea - ther, rough wea - -
rough, rough wea - ther, rough wea - -
rough, rough wea - ther, rough
rough, rough wea - ther, rough wea - -
37
42
- - - - ther, rough wea - ther, rough wea - ther.
- - - - ther, rough wea - ther, rough wea - ther.
wea - - - ther, rough wea - ther, rough wea - ther.
- - - - ther, rough wea - ther, rough wea - ther.
42

47 Moderato
Who doth am - bi - tion shun, And loves to live in the
Who doth am - bi - tion shun, And
Who doth am - bi - tion shun, And
Who doth am - bi - tion shun, And
47 Moderato

50
sun, and loves to live in the sun, and loves,
loves to live in the sun, to live in the sun, and loves, and
loves to live in the sun, to live in the sun, and loves, and
loves to live in the sun, to live in the sun, and loves, and
50

53
loves to live in the sun. Seek - ing the food he eats.
loves to live in the sun.
loves to live in the sun. And
loves to live in the sun. And pleas'd, and
53
56
And pleas'd with
And pleas'd with what he gets, with what he gets, with
pleas'd with what he gets, he gets, with what he gets, with
pleas'd with what he gets, he gets, with what he gets, with
56

59
what he_gets, Seek - ing the_food he eats
what he_gets, and
what he gets, and pleas'd with
what he gets, and pleas'd with what, with
59

62
And pleas'd_with what he_gets, and
pleas'd_with what__ he_ gets, and pleas'd with what he_gets, and
what,_with what he gets, and pleas'd with what he gets, and
what__ he gets, and pleas'd, and pleas'd_with what he gets, and
62

Bars 71 and 73: the original underlay was somewhat erratic, and has been modified.

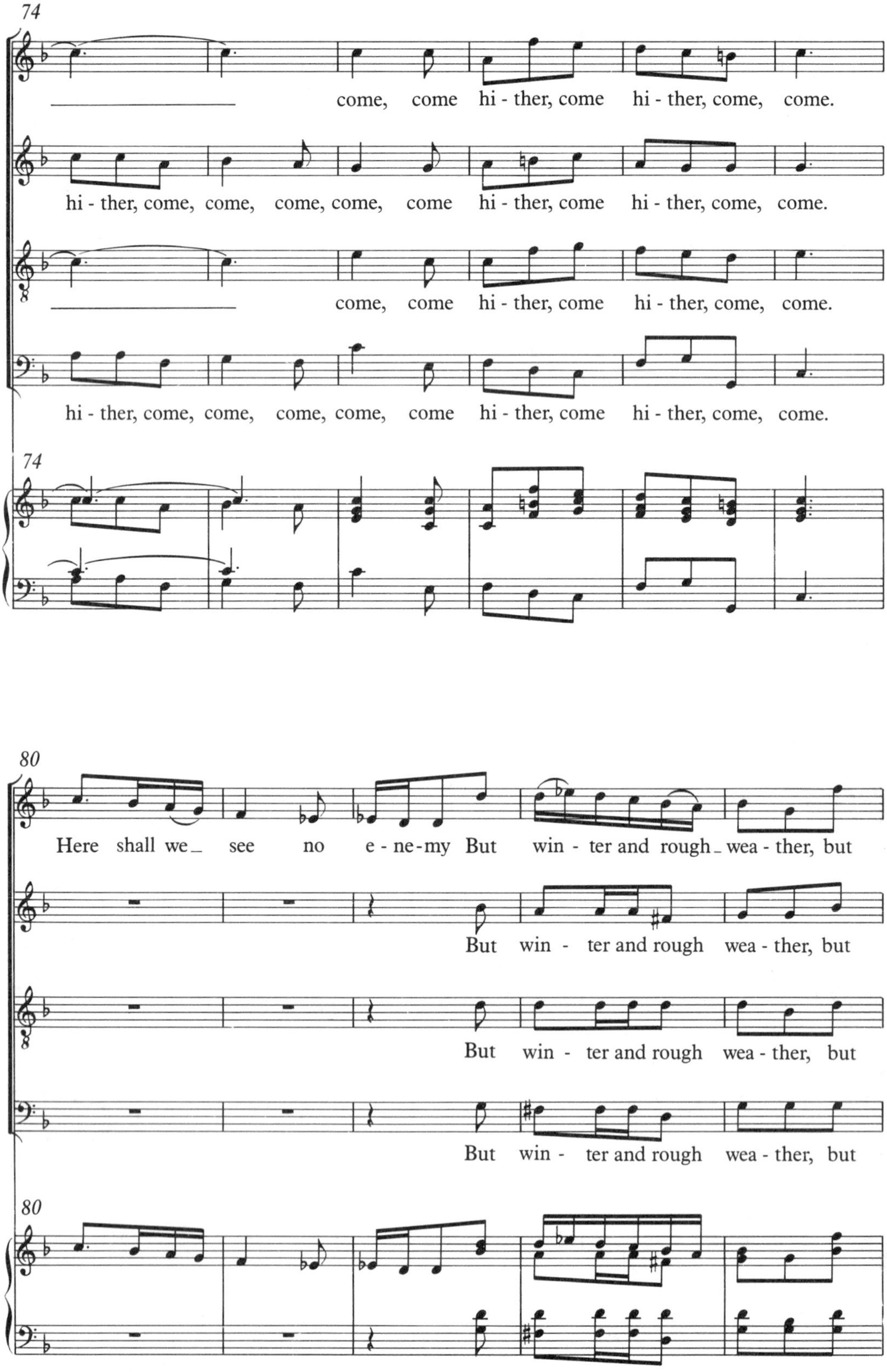

74

come, come hi - ther, come hi - ther, come, come.

hi - ther, come, come, come, come, come hi - ther, come hi - ther, come, come.

come, come hi - ther, come hi - ther, come, come.

hi - ther, come, come, come, come, come hi - ther, come hi - ther, come, come.

74

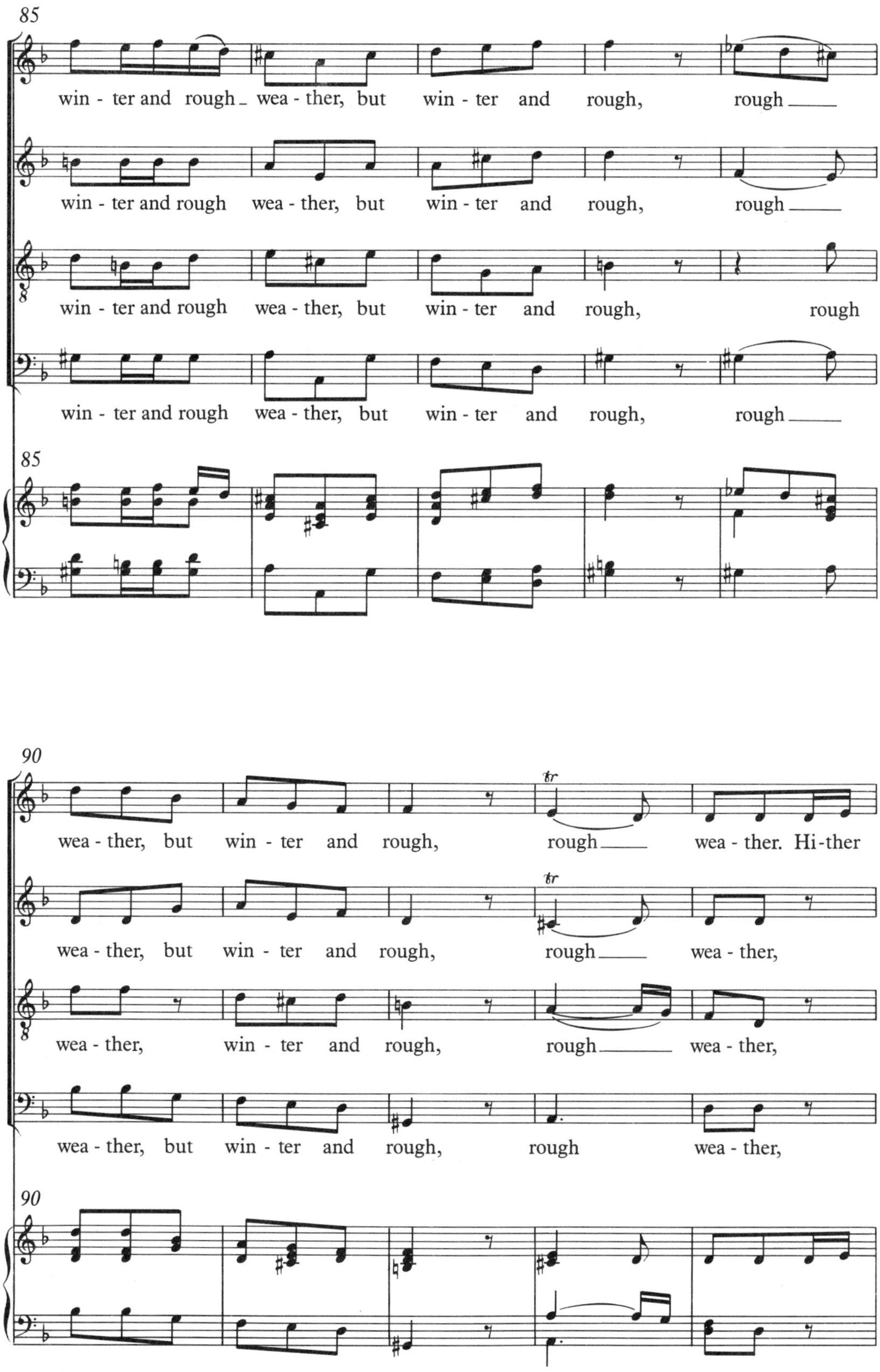

85

win - ter and rough wea - ther, but win - ter and rough, rough

win - ter and rough wea - ther, but win - ter and rough, rough

win - ter and rough wea - ther, but win - ter and rough, rough

win - ter and rough wea - ther, but win - ter and rough, rough

85

95
come, hi-ther come, hi-ther come, come, come, come
Come, hi-ther come, hi-ther come, come hi - ther, come, come, come
Come, come, hi-ther come, come hi - ther, come, come come
Come, come, hi-ther come, come, come, come
95

100
hi-ther, come, come, come hi - ther, come,
hi-ther, come, come hi -ther, hi-ther, come, hi-ther, hi-ther, come, come hi-ther, come,
hi-ther, come, come, come, come, come, hi- ther, come,
hi-ther, come, come, come, come, come, hi - ther, come,
100

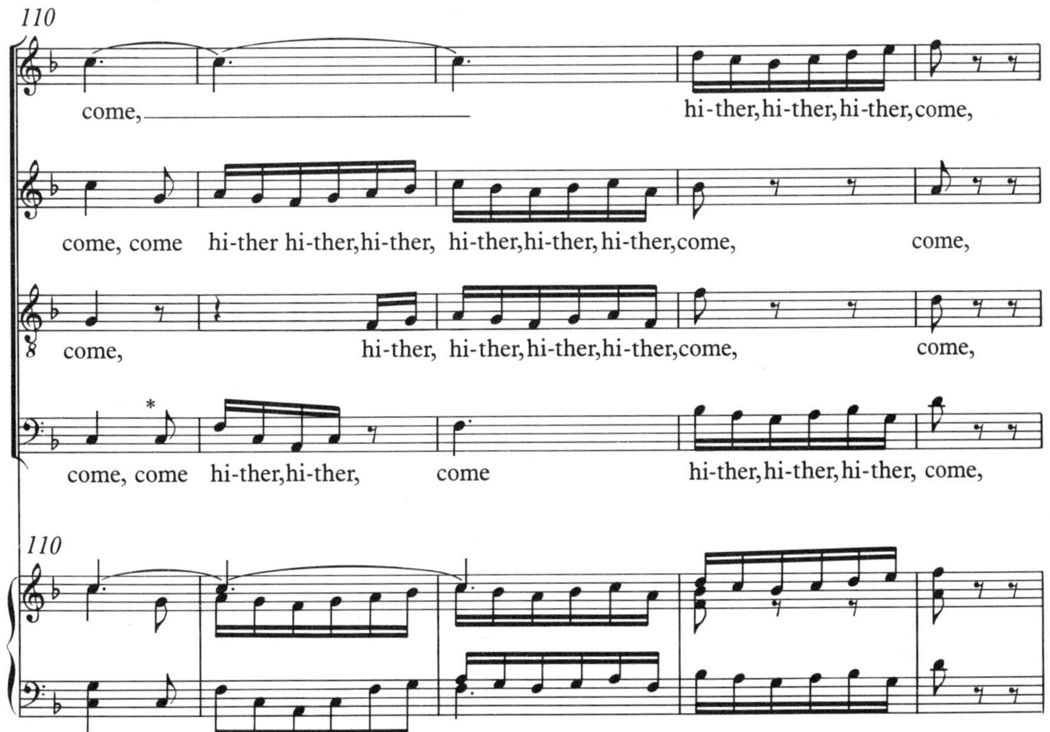

* Bars 110–13: the whole of this phrase was originally in the tenor part.

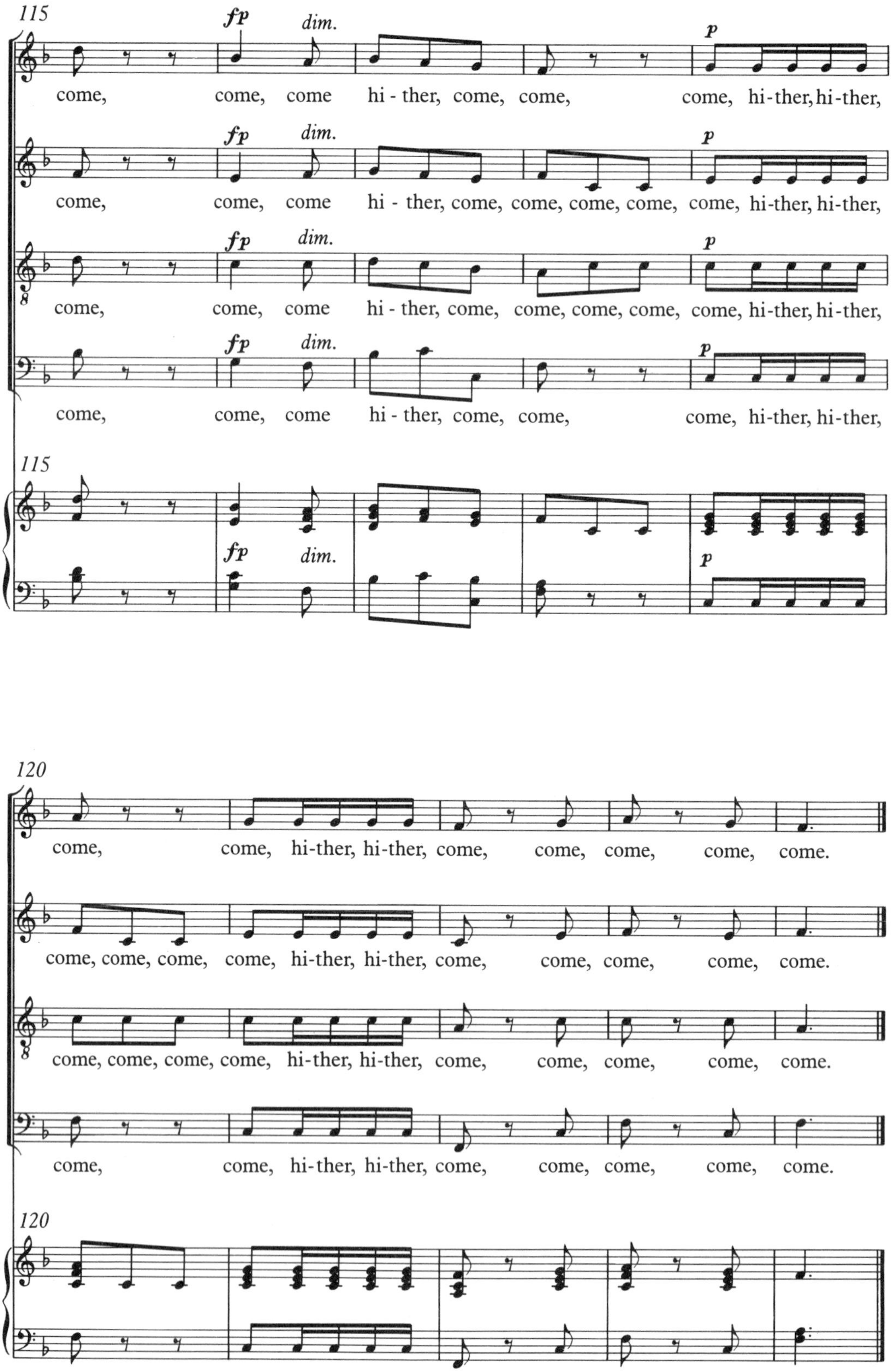

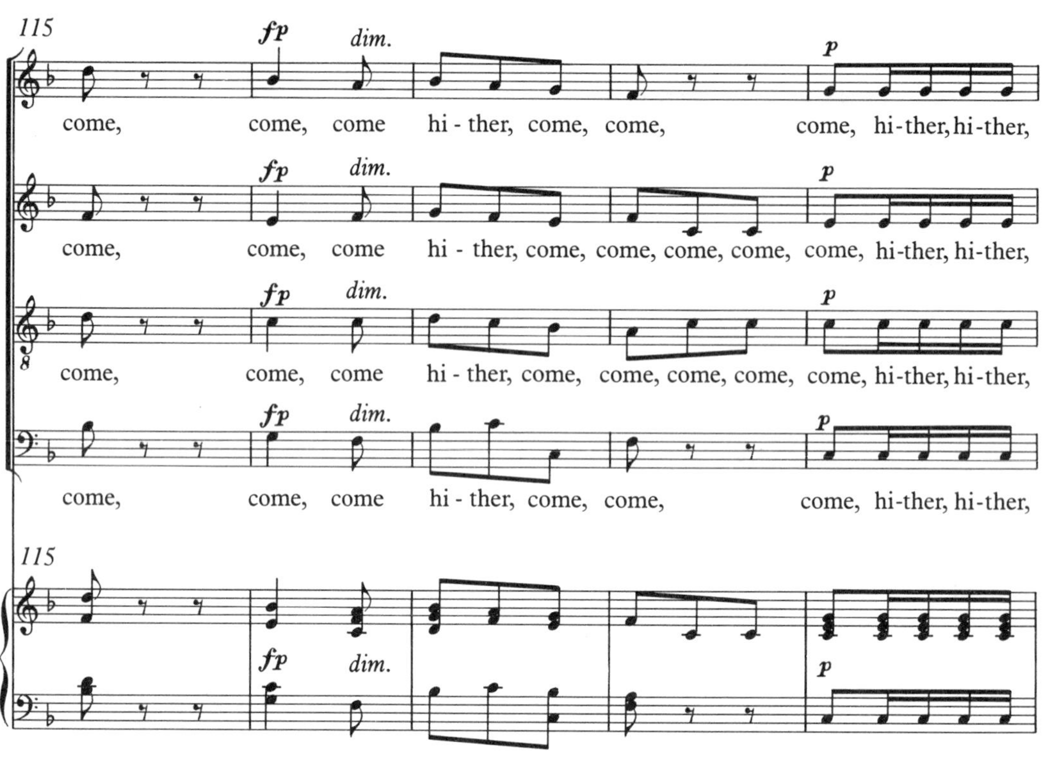

115
fp dim. p
come, come, come hi - ther, come, come, come, hi-ther, hi-ther,
come, come, come hi - ther, come, come, come, come, come, hi-ther, hi-ther,
come, come, come hi - ther, come, come, come, come, come, hi-ther, hi-ther,
come, come, come hi - ther, come, come, come, hi-ther, hi-ther,
115
fp dim. p
120
come, come, hi-ther, hi-ther, come, come, come, come, come.
come, come, come, come, hi-ther, hi-ther, come, come, come, come, come.
come, come, come, come, hi-ther, hi-ther, come, come, come, come, come.
come, come, hi-ther, hi-ther, come, come, come, come, come.
120

22. Hail! smiling morn

ANON.

REGINALD SPOFFORTH
(1768/70?–1827)

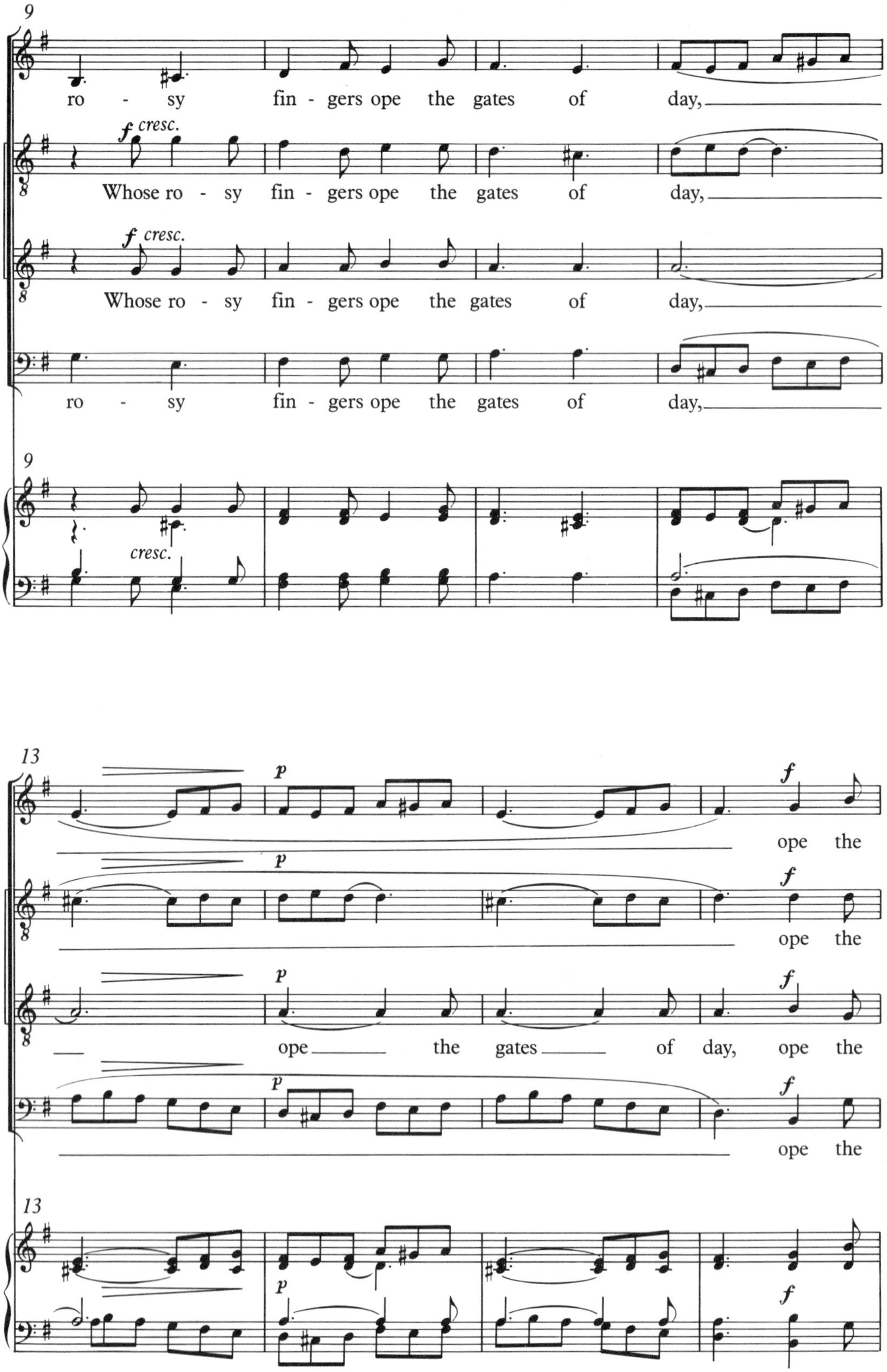

9

ro - sy fin - gers ope the gates of day,

f cresc.

Whose ro - sy fin - gers ope the gates of day,

f cresc.

Whose ro - sy fin - gers ope the gates of day,

ro - sy fin - gers ope the gates of day,

9

cresc.

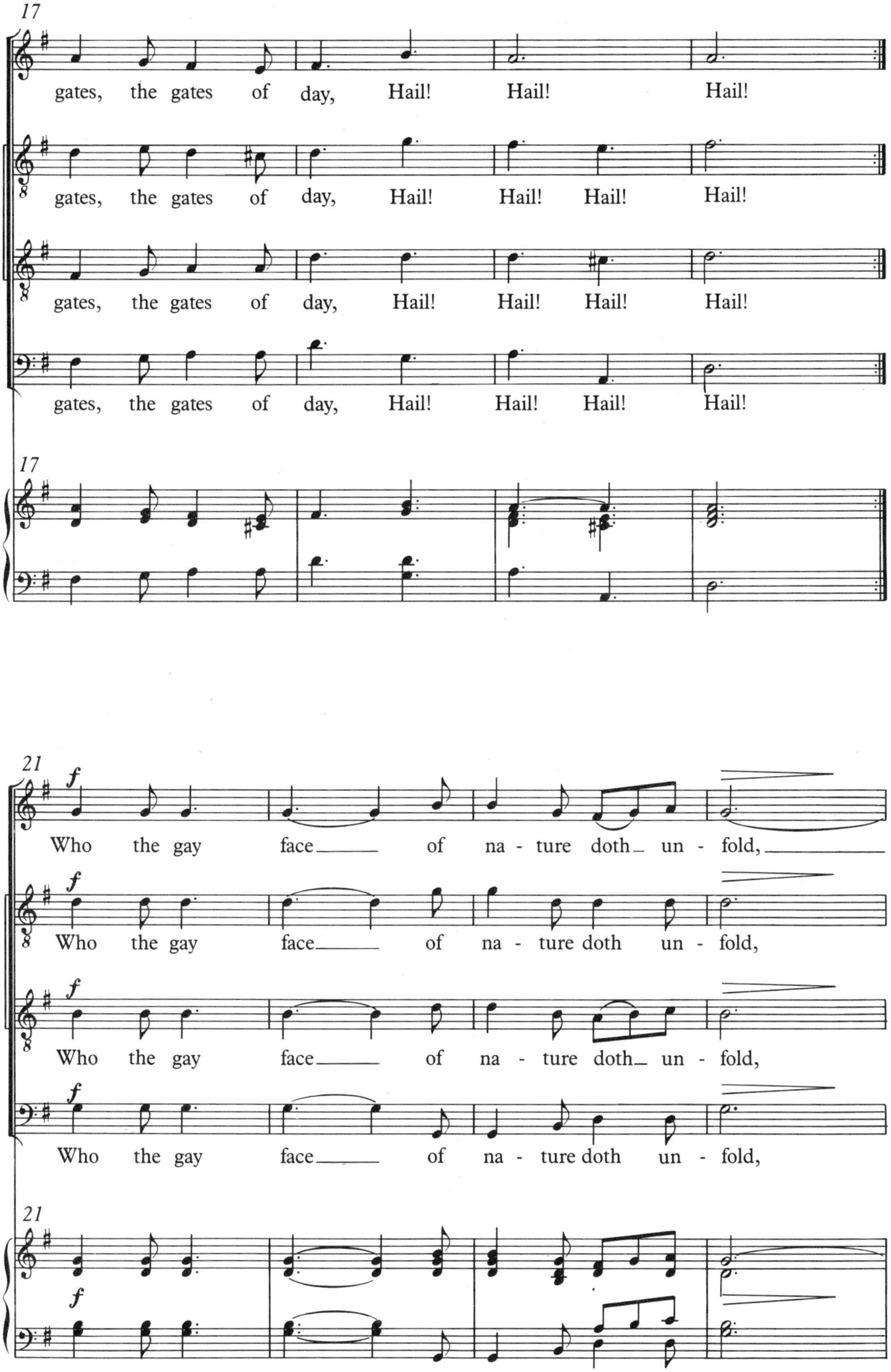

17

gates, the gates of day, Hail! Hail! Hail!

gates, the gates of day, Hail! Hail! Hail! Hail!

gates, the gates of day, Hail! Hail! Hail! Hail!

gates, the gates of day, Hail! Hail! Hail! Hail!

17

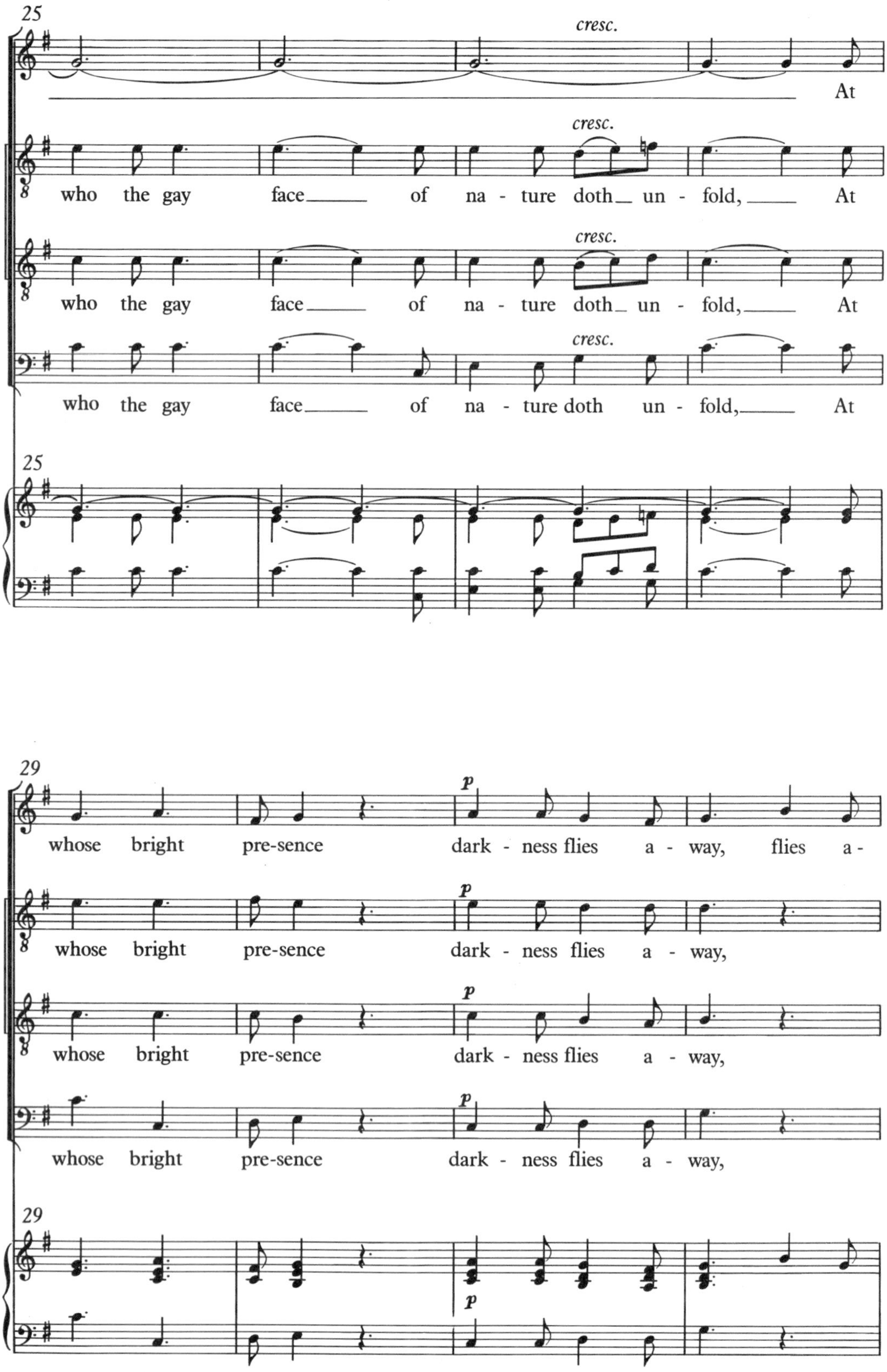

25

cresc.

At

cresc.

who the gay face of na - ture doth un - fold, At

cresc.

who the gay face of na - ture doth un - fold, At

cresc.

who the gay face of na - ture doth un - fold, At

25

33
pp
cresc.
- way, flies a - way, dark -
flies a - way, flies a - way, dark -
flies a - way, flies a - way, dark -
flies a - way, flies a - way, dark -
33
pp
cresc.
37
rall.
Tempo
- ness flies a - way, dark - ness flies a - way, at
- ness flies a - way, dark - ness flies a - way, at
- ness flies a - way, dark - ness flies a - way, at
- ness flies a - way, dark - ness flies a - way, at
37
rall.
Tempo

41

fz *fz*

whose bright pre-sence dark - ness

fz *fz*

whose bright pre-sence dark - ness

fz *fz*

whose bright pre-sence dark - ness

fz *fz*

whose bright pre-sence dark - ness

41

fz *fz*

fz *fz*

45

p *cresc.*

flies a - way, flies a -

p

flies a - way,

p *cresc.*

flies a - way, flies a -

p

flies a - way,

45

p *cresc.*

49

f

- way.

Hail!

cresc.

f

dark - ness flies a - way, dark - ness flies a - way. Hail!

- way.

f

Hail!

cresc.

f

dark - ness flies a - way, dark - ness flies a - way. Hail!

49

f

23. Doubt thou the stars are fire

SHAKESPEARE
(1564–1616)
(*Hamlet*, II. ii)

RICHARD JOHN SAMUEL STEVENS
(1757–1837)

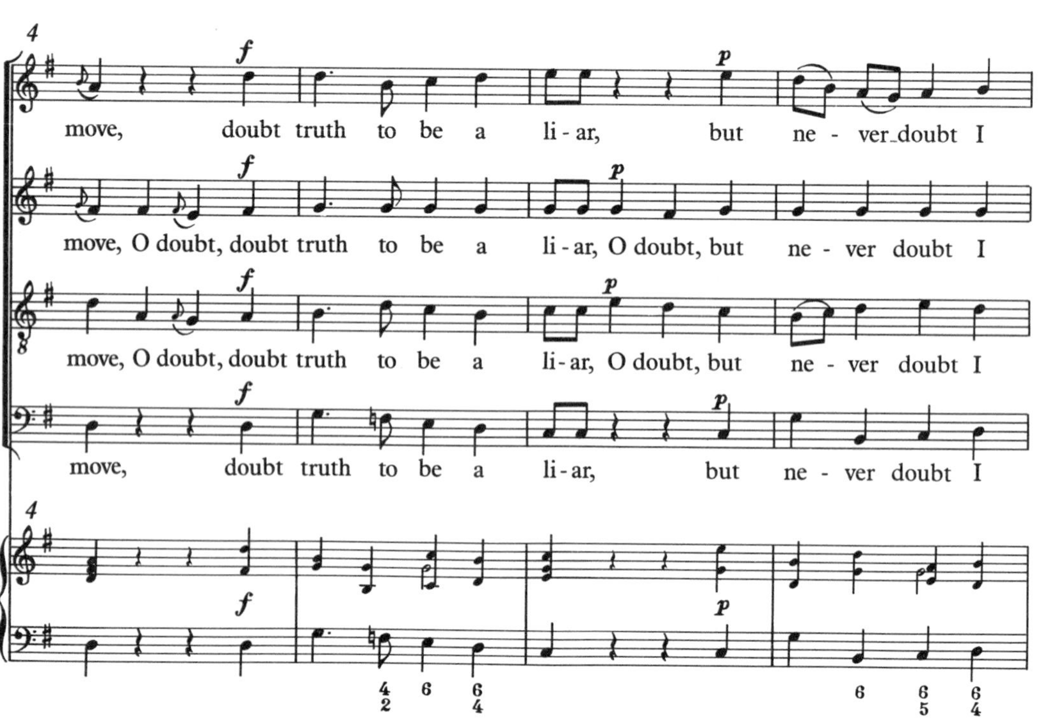

8
f
pp
love, but ne - ver doubt I love, ne'er doubt I love.
love, but ne - ver doubt I love, ne'er doubt I love.
love, but ne - ver doubt I love, ne'er doubt I love.
love, but ne - ver doubt I love.
6 7 6 5 3 7 6 4 5 3 3 6 4 7 2
12
cresc.
p
Doubt thou the stars are fire, doubt thou the sun doth
Doubt thou the stars are fire, doubt thou the sun doth
Doubt thou the stars are fire, O doubt thou, doubt thou the sun doth
Doubt thou the stars are fire, O doubt thou, doubt thou the sun doth
6 6 6 5 6 4 3

15

move, doubt truth to be a li-ar, but ne - ver_doubt I

move, O doubt, doubt truth to be a li-ar, O doubt, but ne - ver doubt I

move, O doubt, doubt truth to be a li-ar, O doubt, but ne - ver doubt I

move, doubt truth to be a li-ar, but ne - ver doubt I

19

love, but ne - ver_doubt_ I love, ne'er doubt I_ love._

love, but ne - ver doubt_ I love, ne'er doubt I love.

love, but ne - ver doubt I love, ne'er doubt I love.

love, but ne - ver doubt I love._

24. Ye spotted snakes

SHAKESPEARE
(1564–1616)
(*A Midsummer Night's Dream*, II. ii)

RICHARD JOHN SAMUEL STEVENS
(1757–1837)

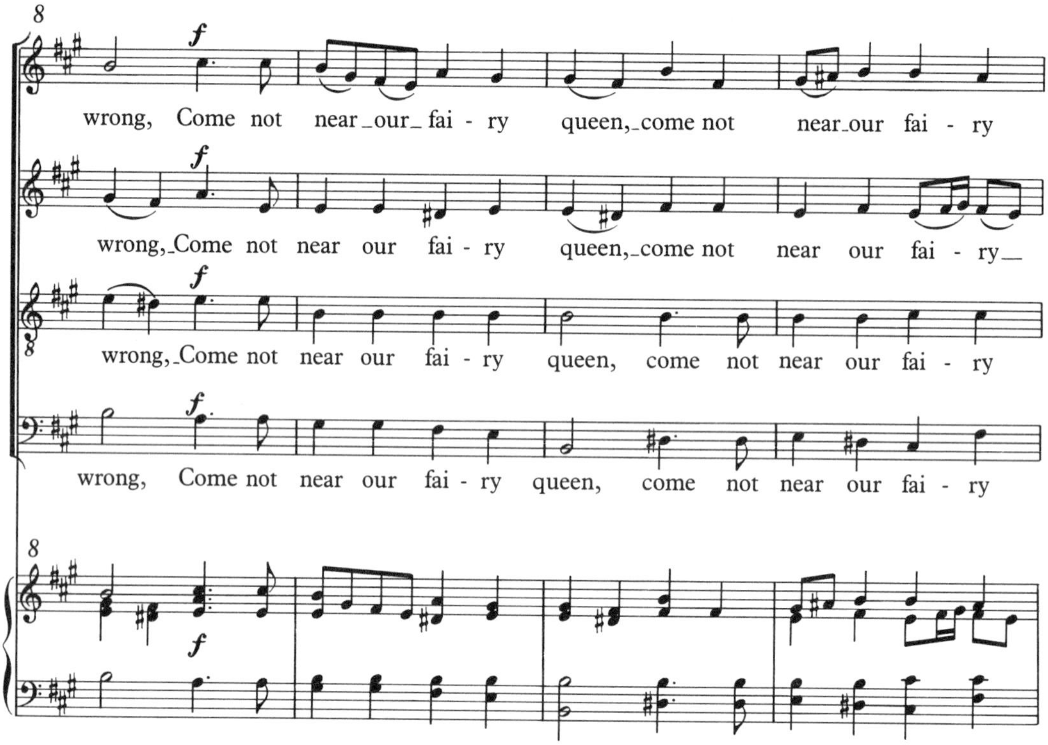

8

f

wrong, Come not near_our_fai - ry queen,_come not near_our fai - ry

f

wrong,_Come not near our fai - ry queen,_come not near our fai - ry_

f

wrong,_Come not near our fai - ry queen, come not near our fai - ry

f

wrong, Come not near our fai - ry queen, come not near our fai - ry

8

f

16
p
cresc.
Sing_ in_ our_ sweet lul - la - by, sing_ in_
[cresc.]
our sweet_ lul - la - by, sing, sing_ in_ our, in
cresc.
lul - la - by, sing,_ sing_ in_ our sweet_
[cresc.]
sweet lul - la - by, sing in
16

19
p
pp
our_ sweet_ lul - la - by; Lul-la, lul-la, lul-la - by, lul-la, lul-la, lul-la -
[p]
pp
our sweet lul - la - by; Lul-la, lul-la, lul-la - by, lul-la -
[p]
pp
lul - la,_ lul - la - by; lul-la - by, lul-la, lul-la, lul-la -
[p]
pp
our_ sweet_ lul - la - by; lul-la - by, lul-la -
19
p
pp

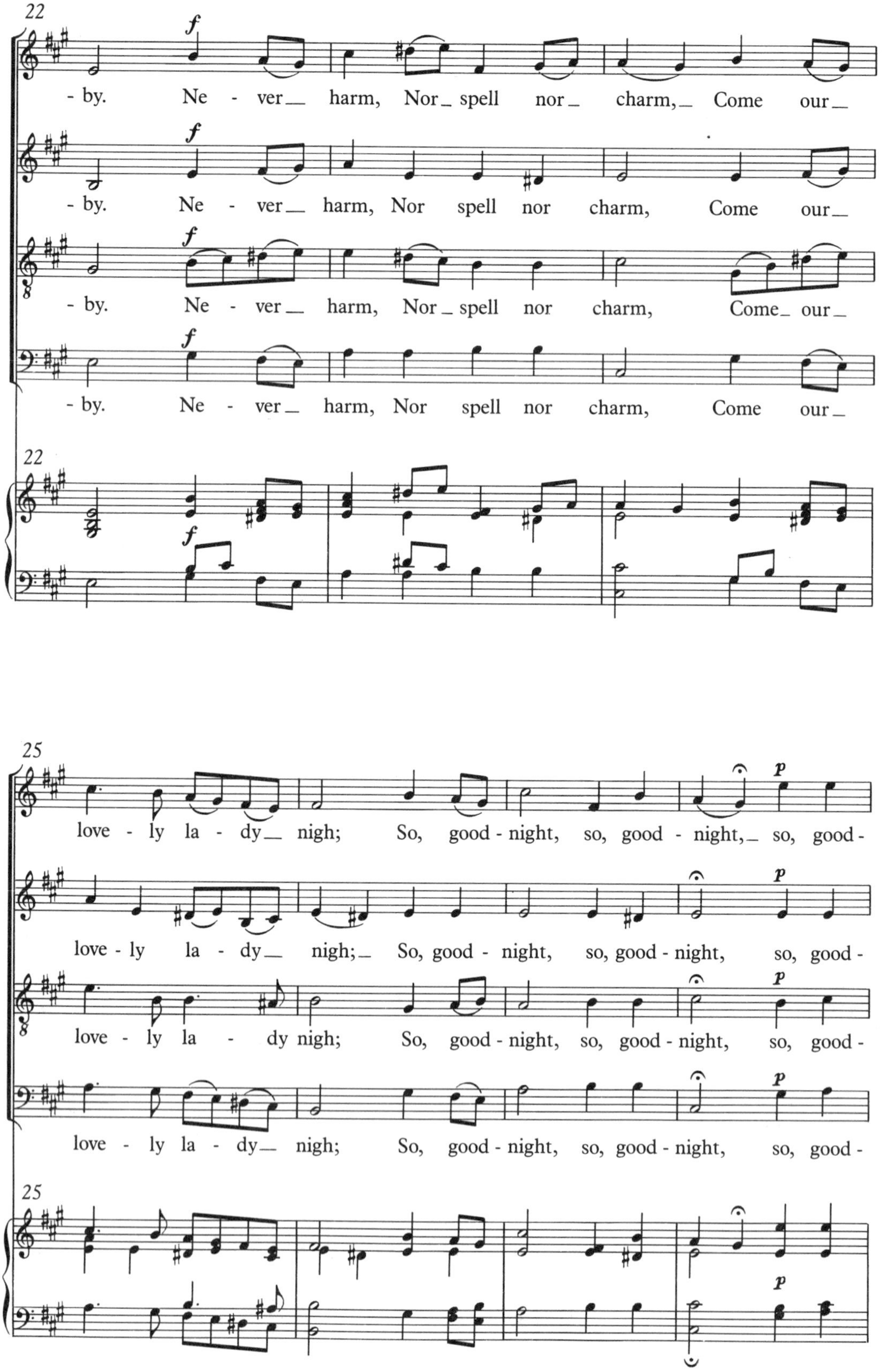

22

- by. Ne - ver_ harm, Nor_ spell nor_ charm,_ Come our_

- by. Ne - ver_ harm, Nor spell nor charm, Come our_

- by. Ne - ver_ harm, Nor_ spell nor charm, Come_ our_

- by. Ne - ver_ harm, Nor spell nor charm, Come our_

29
- night, with lul-la, lul-la - by, lul-la, lul-la, lul-la - by, lul-la, lul-la, lul-la - by.
pp
- night, with lul - la - by, lul-la, lul-la, lul-la - by, lul-la - by.
- night, with lul-la, lul-la - by, lul-la - by, lul-la, lul-la, lul-la - by.
- night, with lul - la - by, lul-la - by, lul-la - by.
33
un poco p
Weav-ing spi-ders, come not here; Hence,
Weav-ing spi-ders, come not here, weav-ing spi-ders come not here; Hence,
[p]
Weav-ing spi - ders, come not here; weav - ing spi - ders, come not here; Hence,
Weav - ing spi - ders, come not here; Hence,
f

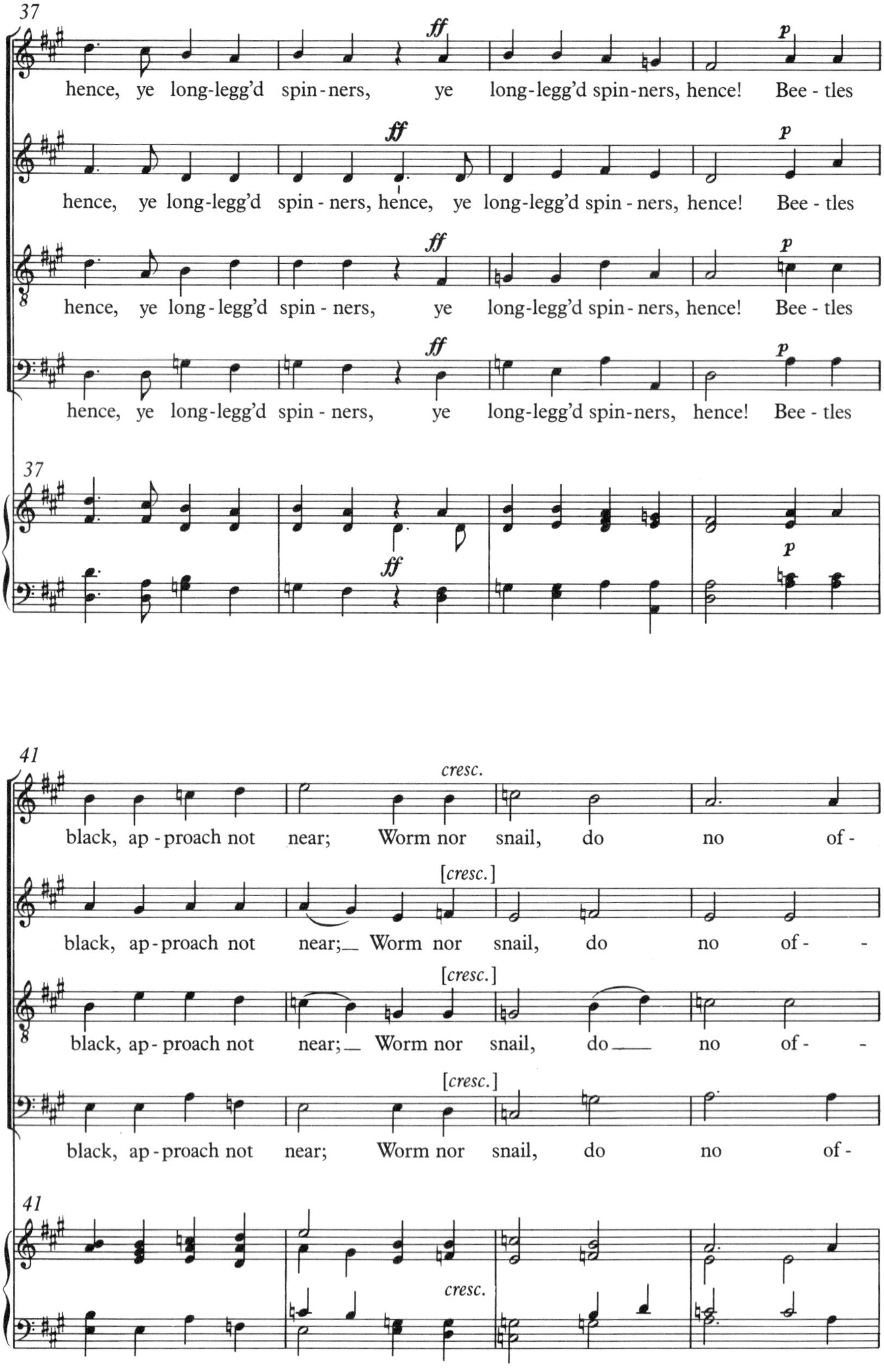

37

ff *p*

hence, ye long-legg'd spin-ners, ye long-legg'd spin-ners, hence! Bee - tles

hence, ye long-legg'd spin - ners, hence, ye long-legg'd spin - ners, hence! Bee - tles

hence, ye long - legg'd spin - ners, ye long-legg'd spin - ners, hence! Bee - tles

hence, ye long-legg'd spin - ners, ye long-legg'd spin-ners, hence! Bee - tles

37

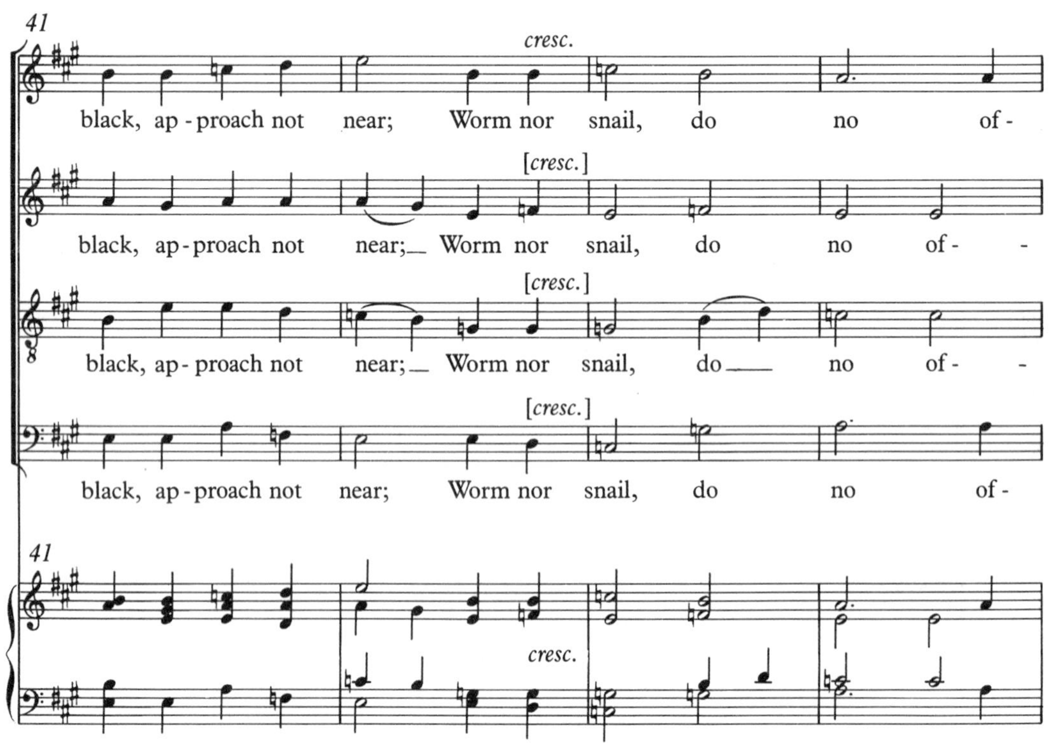

45
-fence, worm nor snail, do no of - fence. Phi - lo-
-fence, worm nor snail, do no of - fence.
-fence, worm nor snail, do no of - fence.
-fence, worm nor snail, do no of - fence.
45
49
-mel, with me - lo - dy
Sing in
Sing in our sweet
Sing in our sweet lul - la - by, sing,
Sing in our sweet
49

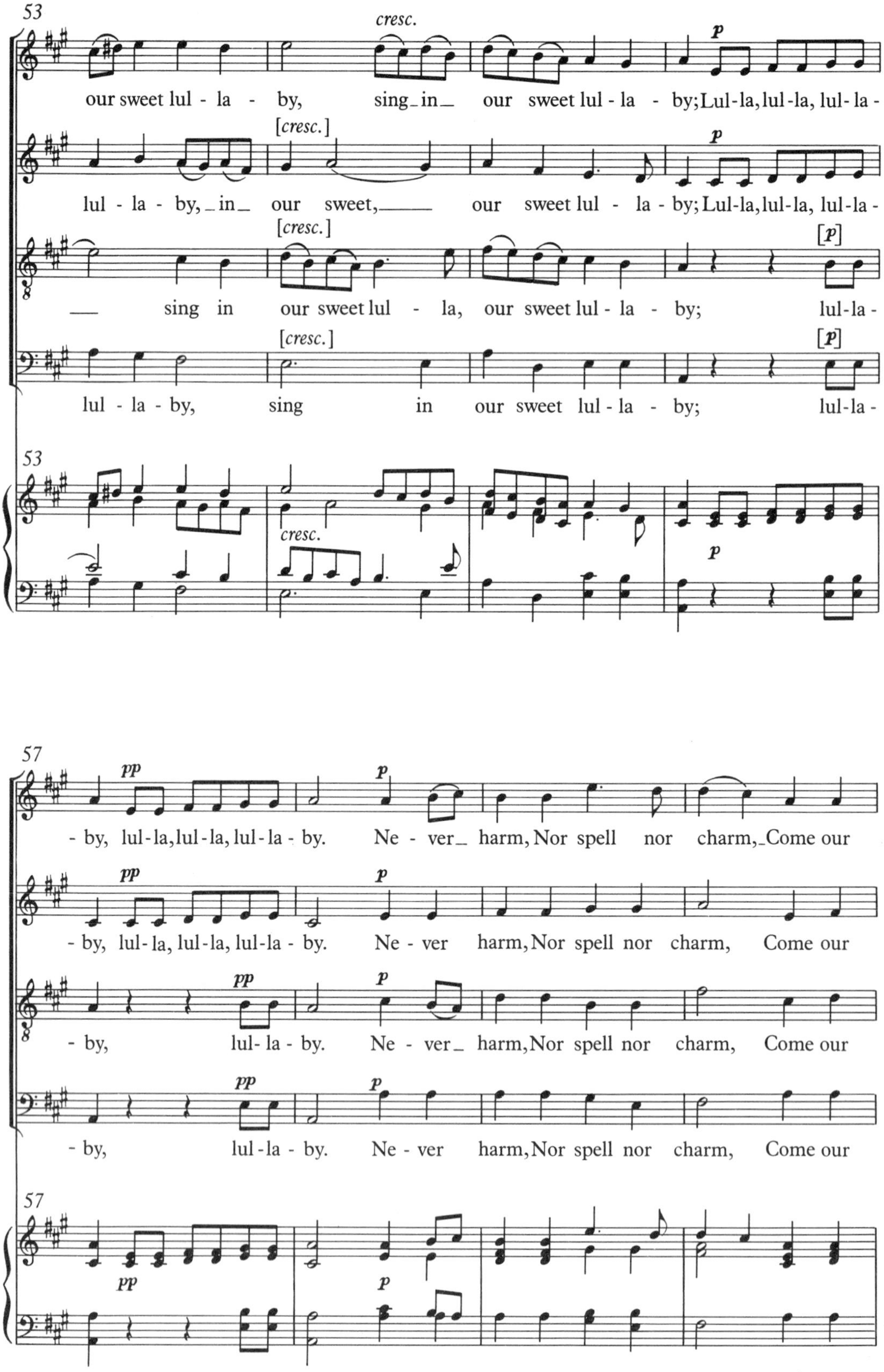

53

cresc.

our sweet lul - la - by, sing_in_ our sweet lul - la - by; Lul-la, lul-la, lul-la -

[cresc.]

lul - la - by,_in_ our sweet,___ our sweet lul - la - by; Lul-la, lul-la, lul-la -

[cresc.]

___ sing in our sweet lul - la, our sweet lul - la - by; lul-la -

[cresc.]

lul - la - by, sing in our sweet lul - la - by; lul-la -

53

cresc.

p

61
un poco cresc.
p
love - ly _ la - dy nigh; _ So, good - night, so, good - night, _ so, good -
[un poco cresc.]
p
love - ly _ la - dy nigh; _ So, good - night, so, good - night, so, good -
[un poco cresc.]
p
love - ly la - dy nigh; So, good - night, so, good - night, so, good -
[un poco cresc.]
p
love - ly _ la - dy nigh; So, good - night, so, good - night, so, good -
61
un poco cresc.
p
65
pp
- night, with lul-la, lul - la - by, lul - la, lul - la, lul - la - by, lul - la, lul - la, lul - la - by.
pp
- night, with lul - la - by, lul - la, lul - la, lul - la - by, lul - la, lul - la, lul - la - by.
pp
- night, with lul - la, lul - la - by, lul - la - by, lul - la by.
pp
- night, with lul - la - by, lul - la - by, lul - la - by.
65
pp

25. When from the skies divine Cecilia came

J. M. MOORE

THOMAS VALENTINE
(1790–1878)

The 'Chorus' designations at bars 29 and 64 may indicate that bars 1–28 and 36–63 can be sung by solo voices if desired.

13
[p]
strain, the melt-ing strain, the
strain, the melt-ing strain, the melt-ing strain, the melt-ing strain, the
p
strain, the deep re-cess-es, deep re-cess-es heard the strain, the
13
p
Tempo primo
17
Slower
[pp]
mf
melt-ing, melt-ing strain, the melt-ing, melt-ing strain; And
pp
melt-ing, melt-ing strain, the melt-ing strain;
melt-ing, melt-ing strain;
17
Slower
Tempo primo
pp
mf
21
[pp]
p
e-cho swept, and e-cho swept each val-ley, hill, and plain, and
[mf]
pp
And e-cho swept each val-ley, hill, and plain,
[mf]
[pp]
And e-cho swept each val-ley, hill, and plain,
21
mf
pp
p

25
e - cho swept each val - ley, hill, and plain.
and e - cho swept each val - ley, hill, and plain.
and e - cho swept each val - ley, hill, and plain.
25
CHORUS 29
Rather quicker
Ce - ci - lia's sons your voi - ces raise, And to the heav'ns re - sound her praise, Ce -
Ce - ci - lia's sons your voi - ces raise, And to the heav'ns re - sound her praise, Ce -
Ce - ci - lia's sons your voi - ces raise, And to the heav'ns re - sound her praise, Ce -
29
Rather quicker
33
- ci - lia's sons your voi - ces raise, And to the heav'ns re - sound her praise.
- ci - lia's sons your voi - ces raise, And to the heav'ns re - sound her praise.
- ci - lia's sons your voi - ces raise, And to the heav'ns re - sound her praise.
33

Larghetto
37
p
En - chant - ing God - dess, en - chant - ing
[p]
En - chant - ing God - dess, en-chant-ing
[p]
En-chant-ing
Larghetto
37
3
p
40
God - dess, shed thy in - fluence here, And
God - dess, shed thy in - fluence here, And
God - dess, shed thy in - fluence here, And
40
44
bid thy dul - cet notes our bo - soms cheer.
bid thy dul - cet notes our bo - soms cheer.
bid thy notes our bo - soms cheer.
44

48
In bonds of harmony, in bonds of harmony, in
In bonds of harmony, in bonds of harmony, in
of harmony our souls unite, in harmony, in
52
bonds of harmony our souls unite, And
bonds of harmony our souls unite,
bonds of harmony our souls unite,
dim.
[dim.]
56
chase fell discord into endless night, and
chase fell discord into night, and
chase fell discord into night, and
[f]
[p]

60
chase fell dis - cord in - to end - less night.
chase fell dis - cord in - to end - less night.
chase fell dis - cord in - to end - less night.
60
CHORUS
Allegro
64
Then shall thy sons their voi - ces raise, And to the heav'ns re-sound thy praise,
Then shall thy sons their voi - ces raise, And to the heav'ns re - sound thy praise,
Then shall thy sons their voi - ces raise, And to the heav'ns re-sound thy praise,
64
Allegro
68
Then shall thy sons their voi - ces raise, And to the heav'ns re-sound thy praise.
Then shall thy sons their voi - ces raise, And to the heav'ns re- sound thy praise.
68
Then shall thy sons their voi - ces raise, And to the heav'ns re - sound thy praise.

26. Divine Cecilia

WILLIAM CONGREVE
(1670–1729)

SAMUEL WEBBE
(1740–1816)

Andante 9
That we to Na - tions yet un- born may prove, to Na-tions yet un -
That we to Na - tions yet un - born, to Na - tions yet un -
Andante 9
13
- born may prove, That Mu-sic on - ly, that Mu-sic on - ly is the food of Love.
- born may prove, That Mu-sic on - ly is the food of Love.
That Mu-sic on - ly, Mu-sic on - ly is the food of Love.
13
Adagio
19
Allegretto
Then shall this day for ev-er sa-cred be To Thee, bright Saint,
Then shall this day for ev-er sa-cred be To Thee, bright Saint, to Thee, bright Saint, to
Then shall this day for ev - er sa-cred be To Thee, bright Saint, to
19
Allegretto

23
to Love and Har-mo-ny. Then shall this day for ev-er sa - cred be To
Love and Har-mo-ny.
Love and Har-mo-ny. Then shall this day for ev-er
23
26
Thee, bright Saint, to Love and Har-mo-ny,
Then shall this day for ev-er sa - cred be To
sa - cred be To Thee, bright Saint, to Love and Har-mo-ny, to
26
29
to Love and Har - mo-ny, for ev-er
Thee, bright Saint, Then shall this day for ev- er sa-cred be, for
Thee, bright Saint, to Thee this day for ev - er, for ev-er
29

32
sa - cred, for ev - er sa - cred be To
ev - er sa - cred, for ev - er sa - cred be To
sa - cred, for ev - er sa - cred, for ev - er sa - cred be To
32
35
Thee, bright Saint, to Love, to Love and Har - mo - ny,
Thee, bright Saint, to Love, to Love and Har - mo - ny, To
Thee, bright Saint, to Love, to Love and Har - mo - ny,
35
39
for ev - er sa - cred be, for ev - er
Thee, bright Saint, to Love, to
Then shall this day for ev - er sa - - -
39

42
f
sa - cred be, then shall this day for ev- er sa-cred
Love, to Love and Har-mo-ny, for ev - er sa - cred
- cred be, then shall this day for ev - er sa - cred _ be,
42
f
45
be To Thee, to Love _ and Har-mo-ny;
be, for-ev - er _ sa - cred To Thee, to Love and Har-mo-ny;
for _ ev - er _ sa - cred be To Thee, to Love and Har-mo-ny;
45
48 Adagio
To Thee, bright Saint, to Love and Har - mo-ny.
To Thee, bright Saint, to Love and Har - mo- ny.
To Thee, bright Saint, to Love and Har - mo-ny.
48 Adagio